HOUSE OF TOMORROW

Author's note:

In order to avoid distress, I have given fictitious names to the children, their relatives and to some of the other characters, localities and institutions which appear in this book. In every other respect, the story is true and the details given are factual. I would add that any deviation I may have made from the truth is one of understating the degree of abuse.

Throughout the book the words 'Care' and 'Children's Home' have been spelt with capital initials when they are being used as the terminology or as the names of institutions of the State Welfare system.

If this story has moved you, the reader, as it moved me, to do something to help Jeanette and her family, or children like those she has helped, or to improve the system that allows such tragedies to happen, you will find at the end of the book a list of ways in which you can do so. Surely as members of Society, we are all responsible for what happens to the children who cannot help themselves.

Jeanette has devoted her whole life to helping a few of the vast numbers in mental or physical pain. For those interested in helping Jeanette's Family, write to Family In Trust, 23 High Street, Ingatestone, Essex, CM4 9DU, who will be pleased to send you information.

C.L.

'... Your children are not your children.
   They are the sons and daughters of Life's longing for itself...
   ... You may give them your love but not your thoughts,
For they have their own thoughts.
   You may house their bodies but not their souls,
For their souls dwell in the house of tomorrow...'

The Prophet by Kahlil Gibran

Foreword

As I put down the first draft of the opening chapters of this
book, I thought very hard about the woman I have known and
loved for so many years – whose ability to give and give, to soak
up other people's pain and grief had, I felt, almost submerged
her own personality. Despite our friendship, I have always been
struck by what a private person Jeanette has been in the
company of other adults. The degree of self-revelation in these
opening chapters, the reliving of intensely painful memories, the
attempt to make sense of them for us must have cost her many
sleepless nights. For such a private person it took a great act of
courage, yet Jeanette's unerring instinct must have directed her
yet again towards the most honest answer – for without these
opening chapters the rest of the book to me would not have
made sense. Jeanette would have appeared to be a saint. Instead,
it is a story of an intensely human person whose one aim is to
rescue other people from an abyss which she herself had to live in
for many years.

My personal hope is that I, together with the other Trustees
of the Family in Trust and Jeanette's many friends, will be able
to continue to give our support to the Family for a long time to
come.

NIGEL EVANS
Television film producer and
Chairman of 'Family in Trust'

Contents

Chapter 1

'Of the (abused) children studied over the years in improved environments, the majority rarely achieved normal intellectual levels... only a few give promise of becoming self-sufficient adults.'
(Dr Elizabeth Elmer, 1967, quoted by Ruth Inglis, Sins of the Fathers, Peter Owen, 1978)

Six months before the outbreak of World War II, Jeanette was born in Balham. There was already one child of three, a pale, thin little boy, and the arrival of another baby was far from a matter for rejoicing. The wage brought in by Jeanette's father, a cobbler, barely catered for the family's needs and her mother took in sewing to augment the meagre income.

Jeanette's earliest memories were of sounds: the noise of her mother's sewing machine whirring intermittently, hour upon hour, in the evenings and into the night; the sound of her brother Alan's coughing – a harsh, rasping cough; and the sound of bombs and anti-aircraft fire as Hitler's assault upon London slowly and methodically crippled the suburbs where they lived.

Like hundreds of other children who had not been evacuated to the safety of the country or to Canada, Jeanette stood with her mother in queues for food and slept in air-raid shelters, accepting their constant hunger and danger as a part of normal life. Her father, whom she barely knew, had been called up and was somewhere abroad with the army. His brief appearances at home on leave brought a tension into the house that she did not understand. She knew only that her mother was unhappy and that her father had no interest in her. Frightened of his unfamiliar, brusque manner and his raised voice, the little girl kept – as far as was possible in the small house – well out of his way.

She retained a sickening memory of an occasion when her father arrived home unexpectedly, absent without leave, and had to be hidden in a cupboard when some soldiers came looking for him. His fear and her mother's were tangible. When the soldiers finally found him and took him away, Jeanette hoped he would not come back. But he did. Most of the population of the country rejoiced when their menfolk were demobbed at the end of the war, but for Jeanette it heralded the start of the terrible rows between her parents. They would go on half the night as her mother shouted her protests at the sexual perversions inflicted on her.

Too young to comprehend the nature of these assaults, Jeanette was nevertheless aware that her father was the perpetrator of pain, and in the morning she would look with horror at her mother's pale face and trembling hands. Her hatred for her father was even greater than her love for Alan and for her younger sister, Betsy.

By the time she was eleven, Jeanette had ceased to ponder why neither of her parents loved her. Since she was a frequent truant from school, she could barely read or write and accepted that she had been born stupid. She was tall for her age, big-boned and ungainly – unlike the pretty, laughing little sister three years her junior, who she adored. She tried always to protect Betsy from her father's violent moods.

Much of the time Jeanette was hungry and she often stole food when she saw the chance. Such money as her father earned was dissipated on fishing gear and clothes for himself, and only her mother's earnings kept them from starvation. Now that Jeanette had grown so much, her mother would use her as a dressmaker's dummy. Evening after evening she had to stand for hours, keeping still whilst her mother tucked and pinned and measured hemlines. Although Jeanette recognised the necessity for this, she hated these tedious sessions, but not so much as she hated the sorties to the dustbins at the end of the road. Her father insisted that she should accompany him on these forays

2

for food for the few chickens they kept in the yard. He would hold the torch whilst he forced her to scrummage amongst the stinking refuse for scraps of food thrown out by their neighbours. Once she was bitten by a rat but he told her to shut up and stop fussing – he'd got used to rats in the war.

But even this ordeal was a mere pinprick of distress compared with the terror evoked each night by her parents' rows. It was not just the bitter chill of the night which caused her to tremble and pull the blanket up to her chin, but the sound of her father's voice which she could hear all too clearly through the thin wall dividing his bedroom from the one in which she lay sleepless. Often it was late at night when the fighting began. The sound of footsteps in the street below would long since have ceased, as would the noise of a back door banging or the screech of a cat as it was turned out for the night. Jeanette's body would be rigid, tense as she waited – and although she longed not to do so – listened for the all too familiar noises.

Now would come her mother's shouted, angry, despairing protests. Jeanette did not know what the words meant, but she could feel the fear in her mother's voice. She would grit her teeth as the first unrecognisable object crashed against the bedroom wall. Now, she told herself, the fight was really beginning.

She would squeeze her eyes tight together, knowing only too well the uselessness of trying to block her ears. Moreover, she was straining to hear if Alan and Betsy had been woken. Alan's coughing told its own tale.

'It'll be over soon,' Jeanette would attempt to comfort herself. But familiarity with the scenario confounded such vain hopes. It would not be over until her mother stopped crying and the bedsprings stopped creaking.

Jeanette did not really understand why these battles took place, any more than she had understood about the war, now over this past four years. She knew that people were glad it was over. She wished it wasn't, for it had brought her father home for good. Once, when she had plucked up courage and asked her mother why her father behaved as he did, she had shrugged her shoulders and said:

'It's on account of the war – the war changed him... he's never been the same since he was in Brussels...'

3

Jeanette never knew what had happened in this remote foreign place called Brussels. Sometimes she wondered if the war had changed other children's fathers in the same way. She did not think so. Her parents were different. She had seen some of the mothers collecting their children from school, smiling, hugging them. Jeanette could not remember ever being embraced or kissed although her mother often hugged Alan and Betsy. Jeanette knew her mother loved them, as deeply as she herself loved Betsy, who was pretty and popular with everyone. Betsy could talk to people but somehow Jeanette was always tongue-tied when people started asking her questions.

She hated it when one of the teachers at school asked her why she hadn't done her homework, why she was often dozing off in class, why she so often played truant. How could she tell them about the tensions at home? How confused and unhappy she was? That last night there'd been a row keeping her awake, or that she'd had to go with her Dad to the dustbins.

It was she who had to rummage in the bins. He didn't care about her and sometimes she hated him as much as she felt he hated her. There were times when she couldn't bear her parents' shouting and she would try to intervene. Then he'd get really angry and shout at her instead.

For weeks on end she would go to school only to register. Not going to school didn't worry her, but missing school dinners did. Often there was no dinner money anyway, but now she'd discovered a way to hang about on the street corner until the dinner queue formed and tag on the end. She'd found ways, too, of stealing the dinner money from the children's coats in the cloakroom; pinching things from shops and taking them down to the pawn shop saying her Mum had asked her to hock them; pinching some woman's purse out of her shopping bag when she wasn't looking. Jeanette had been warned she'd get put in prison if the police caught her, but hunger was a more immediate concern.

Alan said she was stupid because she was so behind with her reading, but now he was trying to teach her. Jeanette was convinced her teachers thought her too dim-witted to learn anything, and she thought they were probably right – she felt stupid, helpless. But Alan insisted he was not prepared to accept

4

a sister who was a moron. He redoubled his efforts, as a result of which Jeanette was soon reading fluently. She now spent a great deal of her time in the public library, mostly because it was warm, but also because books were proving an escape from her real life. She went, too, to the art galleries and, without knowing she was doing so, began to acquire a cultural education.

When the rowing between her parents at night had ceased, she would lie alert and anxious in her bed fighting against sleep. Not only was she prone to nightmares, but all too often she would sleepwalk. There were times when she had been found wandering in the street outside, and she feared this loss of control over her actions. She was obliged to live with the awareness of her inability to stop life being what it was.

There were brief spells when she came close to happiness – when they all seemed united by some family activity or when she was at guides, among her friends, but for the most part such moments were overshadowed by her inborn feeling that she was the unloved family scapegoat. She lived in a state of constant tension.

Once she had come close to asking her Nan to explain her parents' rows. Nan lived a few streets away and if Jeanette dropped in, she would always welcome her and give her bread and dripping, her favourite food.

Occasionally, Jeanette would meet one of her aunts at her grandmother's house. They, too, were kind and one of them often bought the children ice-cream and sweets, but none of them noticed her swollen knee joints or were aware of the ache in all her limbs when she walked to school or to her Nan's. She wished she'd had pneumonia and a bad cough like Alan's, which people noticed and sympathised with; but because she was withdrawn and uncommunicative and so seldom happy, those around her were accustomed to her downcast face and put her occasional complaints about the pain in her legs down to an attempt to gain attention. She was told not to make up such silly stories and to stop fussing. Not until four or five years later, when she was admitted to hospital with anaemia, was the reason for her swollen joints discovered. She also had myocarditis – a complication of rheumatic fever – which explained her childhood years of pain.

But for the present, her mother saw no need to take Jeanette to doctors, nor even to go herself when she suspected Jeanette's father might have broken one of her ribs. He'd be in serious trouble if the authorities found out, get put in prison, her mother had said, and then where would they be without his pay packet and only her meagre earnings to support them all?

'Like as not, you kids would be put in Homes,' her mother warned repeatedly, 'and we'd all be split up!'

So Jeanette said nothing more about her legs, for who would take care of Betsy if *she* were not there to protect her?

The frequencies of the rows at night did not diminish with time. More often than not, Jeanette went to bed hungry and fearful, sleep eluding her. Somewhere out in the darkness, a tomcat might yowl or a dog bark. In a way, it was scary and yet comforting to know she wasn't the only living thing in the world lying awake. Her thoughts would wander to the next day's problems. If she went to school in the morning, she would be certain to doze off and get told off by the teacher. Maybe she'd skip school and go down to the shops. However cold the day, it was always warm in Woolies – and maybe she'd be able to pinch a packet of biscuits or a bar of chocolate; maybe someone would leave their purse on a counter with hundreds and hundreds of pounds in it. Then she could buy everything Alan, Betsy and her mother would ever need; the big doll with the yellow hair for Betsy; a new set of darts for Alan. Maybe there'd be enough so her Mum never again had to make another dress for anyone and she could take the sewing machine with its relentless treadle down to the pawn shop and get even more money for it. Maybe there'd be enough money so they didn't need what her father earned and he'd go away, far, far, far away to that place called Brussels where he'd been in the war one time, and never, ever, ever come back.

When Jeanette was eleven they moved to a different house in Morden. She went to a different school, too, but nothing else changed. Mostly she did not go to school, and was hopelessly behind with her work. When asked why she often played truant, she muttered whatever reply came into her head. It didn't seem to matter much what she said since she couldn't talk about the things that were really bad in her life, such as the violent rowing between her parents. After one particularly violent scene, her father had stormed out of the house. Jeanette had stood at the window of the bedroom she now shared with Betsy, hoping, as always, that he would *never* come back, but knowing that he would. He always did. In the next bedroom, Alan was systematically throwing darts into his door, as powerless as she to do anything to stop the fights. Downstairs, her mother was sweeping up the glass from a broken window and the neighbours standing outside their houses were beginning to disperse. One of them had been laughing as she called out: 'Well, I'm off, the excitement's over...' The scene was as familiar to them as to Jeanette and no one bothered about the shouting unless it reached the point where missiles were hurled and real violence was evident. Mostly, the neighbours were only mildly curious and didn't interfere – it was a domestic row which didn't concern them.

Alan was very clever and in Jeanette's opinion, knew most things. But he never explained the mystery of what their father did to their mother that made her cry out. When she'd been younger, Jeanette had longed to be grown up so she could leave home, run away and get a job and take Betsy with her. Now she never wanted to grow up and marry and have to go through what her mother went through year after year. There were small mounds where Jeanette's breasts were beginning to grow and hair where there'd been none before. She watched her body with dread, knowing that there was nothing she could do to halt the processes of nature.

'It won't be long before you start your monthlies,' her mother told her. 'Then you'll have to watch out what you do with boys or next thing you'll be pregnant!'

Jeanette didn't much care what happened to her. She wished fervently that she could die. She wanted to escape the turmoil of her existence; it would be lovely just to go to sleep and never wake up again.

Her only consolation for living was that she was there to take care of Betsy. If she were not around to take the brunt of her father's temper, he might start on her sister. The war had been over for six years and her father hadn't changed – at least not towards her mother. Just lately, however, he'd taken to staring at Jeanette in an odd way. She hated his eyes – cold, blue, empty – and her body would break out in a sweat if she looked up and found him staring. It was to mark the beginning of a fear that far outweighed her former spells of unhappiness. Her father now found in her a new outlet for his enjoyment.

At first, she could not understand why one afternoon he told her to go upstairs; but when he followed her into her bedroom, she realised his intention. She was eleven years old when he first sexually assaulted her. The searing physical pain was as nothing compared to the emotional conflict raging within her. She felt as if her very spirit was being crushed out of existence.

Her father seemed unaware of her feeling of total degradation; was deaf to her protests, blind to her tears. In a last despairing hope that she could plead with him to stop, she opened her eyes. His cold, blue ones stared down at her without pity.

When her ordeal finally ended, he threatened her with the consequences were she to reveal the facts.

'If you tell your mother, it'll be your fault if we're all split up. You kids will be taken away . . . put in Homes. From now on it's a secret between us, see? Don't you dare tell no one! Not if you know what's good for you!'

He showed no sign of guilt or remorse. After he had gone, she lay for a minute or two, sobbing quietly. She was old enough to know that there was no escape from the horror of her situation: her father had the power to do exactly as he pleased and she knew that it would happen again and again. Her hatred of him exceeded pity for herself.

Jeanette faced reality as the tears dried and she tried to wash away the shame. There was no one in the world who could protect her – least of all her mother who couldn't even protect herself . . .

Jeanette's emotional conflict was unbearable. She now found a means of escape from reality. She discovered a stream in a park a few miles away and for the next three years it was there she spent most of her time – time which should have been spent in school. There, alone, she lost herself in a world of fantasy, imagining that she was the child of parents who were happy to have a daughter like herself, who loved her, who loved each other.

The dream was very vivid, but could offer only a temporary refuge from the torment of the real world in which she lived.

Chapter 2

'It was not until 1933 – fifty-seven years later than in America – that Parliament passed a Bill which made it possible in Britain to prosecute parents for cruelty to their children.'
(Ruth Inglis, Sins of the Fathers, *Peter Owen, 1978)*

Jeanette loaded the last of four rickety kitchen chairs on to the lorry and paused to watch as her mother came out of the house and dumped a broken table on to the growing pile of household items and rubbish by the front gate. This was the day they were due to be evicted and the bailiffs might arrive at any moment to turn them on to the street and impound their possessions. They would fetch a few pounds at most, Jeanette thought bitterly. But unless luck was against them, there would be nothing much left for the men to take; her mother had arranged for a friend to come round with his small lorry into which they were cramming as many necessary items of furniture as it would hold. As soon as possible, they would be on their way to the hop fields in Kent and the bailiffs would have nothing but the house to repossess.

Jeanette felt no bitterness about their eviction. Since her father had left them three years previously, they had got deeper and deeper into arrears with the rent. His only legacy had been another child, a little boy, Dan, who was born not long after he had walked out... and the debts. Dan had been put into a Home by their mother whilst they tried to arrange new accommodation in one of the hop-pickers' huts.

With another mouth to feed, there had been no chance of the

family finances improving over these past few years. Young though Alan was, he had married and set up home with his wife, and had therefore been unable to make a contribution to the family budget. Jeanette herself had managed to contribute something. She had had a variety of jobs – in a greengrocer's, in a toy factory, in a sweetshop, in a baker's and as a cashier at the Co-op; but her weekly wage had been too small to make much difference. As for their mother's earnings as a seamstress, they had usefully augmented their father's wage, but were totally inadequate as a means of keeping the family out of debt. Betsy, who was still at school, was too young to have made any contribution. That morning she had been sent round to their Nan's to keep her out of the way.

As Jeanette returned to the house to collect a small pile of faded cretonne curtains to take out to the lorry, she reflected that she herself had no regrets about leaving their home. She would be happy to put behind her the dreadful memories it held for her. It was a long while since her father had finally walked out for good after one last blazing row, but time had not softened her memories. She had been fourteen years old when at last she had plucked up the courage to tell her mother of the private hell she had been living in since she was eleven. Betsy was growing up and Jeanette had feared that her father might soon turn his hateful demands either to her sister or to one of the friends she sometimes brought home. Her confession had obliged her mother to confront him, and he had walked out – for good, Jeanette prayed. Even now, she was still afraid he might suddenly reappear in their lives; in this respect their departure today for an unknown destination was a blessing since he would no longer know where to find them.

Whilst Jeanette had been serving in the greengrocer's shop, one of the customers who felt sorry for the morose, ungainly girl, had asked her what she wanted to do with her life now that she had left school.

'You should get yourself a residential post,' the woman had suggested. 'If you go down to the Advice Centre, they'll likely help you find something!' But Jeanette felt she could not bring herself to desert her mother, Betsy and her young brother.

Recently, her mother had started openly to blame her for the

11

predicament they were now in. But for Jeanette, she said, their father would not have deserted them and they would not now be in this financial mess; it was Jeanette's fault that they were being evicted...

Filled with a sense of bitterness at this injustice – and yet unable to rid herself of the belief that she *was* guilty in some way – Jeanette was now impatient to leave the past behind her. Her bitterness gave way to a feeling of agonising embarrassment as she became aware that behind their curtains, the neighbours were watching the family's attempts to beat the bailiffs to it by removing whatever the small lorry could hold. Much would have to be left behind and the heap by the pavement was growing. Occasionally a passer-by would stop to look over the pile and ask if they could take an unwanted item which they could make use of. Someone took a worn broom, another an old fire-guard.

The lorry was by now bulging with its load. The driver came out of the shed carrying a girl's bicycle and flung it on the dump. It was one Jeanette and Alan had built for Betsy from bits and pieces they had searched for with painstaking care from scrap heaps and junk yards, and it was Betsy's most treasured possession. Jeanette darted forward as an onlooker reached out a hand to take it.

'That's Betsy's bike!' she yelled. 'You can't have that!'

Her mother's protest that there was no room for it on the lorry was to no effect. Jeanette clung tightly to the handlebars as the passer-by tried to remove it.

'Don't you dare take it – it's my sister's,' she shouted, her normally pale face flushed a dark angry red. 'Put it down, you bastard! It's hers!'

Encouraged by her mother's repeated insistence that there was no room for the bike, the stranger tried to prise Jeanette's fingers from the handlebars.

'You aren't fucking taking it – not Betsy's bike!' Jeanette yelled even louder.

The man hesitated, taken aback by her insistence. Suddenly the girl released her grip and made a dive for a heavy hammer leaning up against the wall beside a coal shovel and a bundle of flue brushes. Jeanette picked up the hammer and ran back with it. Lifting it high above her head, she brought it down on the rickety old bike with all the force of her pent-up anger. The rusty metal buckled, crumpled and, at the third blow, broke apart.

A feeling of triumph welled through her.

'Ain't no one gonna have it if Betsy can't!' she shouted as she raised the hammer yet again.

The stranger, her mother and the lorry driver glanced at one another helplessly. There was no point now in loading the pathetic remnants of the bicycle on to the lorry. Shrugging his shoulders, the stranger wandered off.

'Will you stop mucking about and do something useful!' Jeanette's mother said, her voice a mixture of irritation and anxiety. 'We'll have the bailiffs on us in a minute. Put that bloody hammer in the lorry and get in. It's time we were off!'

Jeanette's anger evaporated as she obeyed her mother's instructions. It was, after all, silly to care, she thought as she climbed into the lorry. What did it matter? What did anything matter? If the bailiffs did turn up before they got away, it would be her fault – just as everything else was her fault.

'We'll borrow a few things from your Nan when we collect Betsy!' her mother said in a quiet, hopeless voice. 'At least we'll be in Kent before the regular pickers, so we'll get ourselves a hut.'

The weather was fine when they arrived at their destination as August drew to an end. As predicted, the hundreds of hop-pickers who came down from London for the harvesting season had not yet arrived and there were only the regular labourers about the farm. But before long, every hut was occupied with families of the migrant workers and gipsies, and there was no hope of any privacy.

Jeanette missed the solitude of her private place by the stream in the park where she could be alone, and was more than ever determined to find a residential job somewhere, anywhere. She hated it when people spoke to her and tried to involve her in their conversations. But soon the picking started and the urgent need for money impelled them to work as long hours as possible. The men cut the bines whilst the women and children stripped the branches of their clusters of hops, each family filling their own baskets.

The pay was ten pence a bushel and although at first it did not

13

seem particularly exacting work, after a while the pickers' wrists would begin to ache and to become inflamed. Some of the pickers developed hop-rash caused by the irritative effect of the bines on their skin; some had inflamed eyes brought on by the chemicals with which the hops had been dusted. There were, too, the inevitable stings and insect bites, and scalds and burns as they cooked their evening meal over open fires at night. Many of the children got diarrhoea and stomach upsets, either from eating apples they had scrumped from the orchards or unfamiliar poisonous berries they found in the hedgerows, or because of the unhygenic methods of their parents' cooking.

Jeanette's mother enjoyed the company of the other families who gathered round their fires in the evenings to eat, sing and gossip; but Jeanette kept to herself. She knew she was different from all the others, ugly, unclean; if they knew what had happened to her, they would consider her to be disgraced. It was easier to avoid conversation, questions, probings into her feelings and thoughts. She felt responsible for all that had happened – to her, to her mother, and for the terrible uncertainty of their future as a family. It did not occur to her to blame her father who her mother always exonerated.

'Wasn't his fault, Jeanette! Your Dad was never the same when he came back from Brussels after the war. Did something to him, it did, out there. He weren't the same after that.'

Jeanette was convinced the fault was hers. It didn't surprise her that her father had thought so little of her that he could do those terrible things. She believed she was stupid and clumsy, and she hated her tall ungainly appearance. She feared that Betsy, too, would see her as she saw herself. Betsy made lots of friends wherever she went. Often when someone caught sight of the girl, they would say, 'She'll break a few hearts when she's a bit older!' Jeanette's one comforting thought to which she clung was the knowledge that her father had gone and wasn't likely ever to come back.

She decided the time had come for her to take the advice once given her – to try to obtain a residential job. But her complete lack of self-confidence meant she must draw on every reserve of courage to present herself at the local Advice Centre. She was

14

painfully aware that she had no qualifications, and she could imagine what her school report would be like – not one single O-level to her credit; but with domestic help hard to come by, it was not long before the Advice Centre found a living-in job for her at a Dr Barnado's Home in Essex. Like a small village, the Home comprised a number of different houses run by married couples, each accommodating twelve to fourteen children. The couple for whom Jeanette went to work also had two children of their own so there was no shortage of work for her. A general dogsbody, she helped with the cooking, did the washing, laid tables, helped to bath and feed the younger children. When she was not on duty, she hitchhiked to the hop fields where her mother still lived with little Dan, who had been retrieved from the Home.

At the end of September, Jeanette's mother moved with other families to a nearby farm where fruit picking was in progress, once more living in one of the vacant hop-huts. The owner's wife was in need of domestic help and although the pay was very poor, she took the job since she and Dan were permitted to live in one of the huts in return for her services.

With her mother busy for long hours at the farmhouse, Jeanette took care of Dan on her visits to see them. She felt the same deep, protective love for him as she had always felt for her young sister. On one such visit, which Jeanette would never forget, one of the farm dogs attacked Dan. In an instant, his mother gathered up the child and held him aloft. But the dog, balked of its intended prey, now attacked the terrified woman, mauling, biting, tearing at her legs like a wild animal as it tried to reach the little boy.

Now began a period of acute worry and added responsibility for Jeanette. Her mother went back and forth to hospital whilst the doctors tried to repair the terrible damage the dog had inflicted. The owners did not want the animal shot and, despite the fact that they had lost the services of Jeanette's mother, in return for the family's silence, they were allowed to remain in the hut.

Jeanette was deeply impressed by the care and efficiency of the nurses who looked after her mother at the hospital. For some time she had felt an insistent need to do something more

15

worthwhile with her life, and now the urge to become a nurse took hold of her. Soon after her nineteenth birthday, she applied to the matron of the Queen Victoria Hospital in East Grinstead and, with the aid of an excellent reference from her employers at Dr Barnado's, she was able to obtain a place there on a pre-nursing course.

Jeanette found herself assigned to the burns unit as an auxiliary nurse. Here the brilliant Archibald McIndoe worked his miracle plastic surgery on the terribly burned patients who were brought there from all over the country in the hope that his skills could lessen their disfiguration. Although Jeanette's work was once more that of a dogsbody, she nevertheless learned from observing the doctors and nurses as they tended their patients, and felt even more certain that she wanted to take up nursing as a career.

Meanwhile, she felt totally isolated because of her 'difference' from ordinary girls. Still convinced that she was bad, that her body was dirty, that she was indisputably guilty, she lived in constant fear less the truth about her past should be discovered. Overriding the sense of shame was this desperate fear of exposure. She suffered, as always, from nightmares and knew that she talked in her sleep. Terrified lest she should reveal her evil secret, she would never share a room with other students, and fiercely resisted any attempts by them to satisfy their friendly curiosity as to her childhood and family. It would be many years before Jeanette learned that this self-imposed isolation from her contemporaries was a typical reaction of a victim of sexual abuse. She was happiest in impersonal relationships with the patients.

But slowly she was drawn into a superficial friendship with a girl of her own age called Angela who was engaged to be married to a young soldier. Angela's fiancé had a twin brother, Daryl, and since he had no current girlfriend, Jeanette reluctantly agreed to join the other couple and go out with Daryl as a foursome.

Before long, she discovered that not only did she like him as a person but that she enjoyed talking to him, although her rôle was more often that of a listener since she could never talk about herself. Gradually, Daryl became convinced that he was in love

16

with this strange, remote girl, and proposed marriage. He seemed so anxious that she should marry him that Jeanette finally agreed to become engaged.

Until then Jeanette had managed somehow to keep her ardent boyfriend at arm's length. Perhaps he had put her reluctance for any close physical contact between them down to shyness. She had been unable to explain to him – or indeed to herself – her total revulsion every time he touched her. She longed to drag her hand away when he held it, longed to shrug off his arm if he put it round her shoulders. Her hands and lips clenched tightly and her body would break out in a cold sweat each time he kissed her. Because she was fond of him and wanted so much to be like Angela – a normal girl in love – she had endured these physical demonstrations of affection.

But now the relationship changed. Not unnaturally, Daryl's thoughts and conversation turned to the future – their future. He was aware that Jeanette was devoted to her young brother.

'I know you love kids and I want them, too,' he told her one evening. 'I'd like four boys. Wouldn't it be great, Jan – four sons?'

Jeanette's instant reaction was one of dismay. The thought of children forced her to consider the side of marriage that she had deliberately blanked out from her consciousness. Babies were conceived as a result of a sexual union, the very thought of which horrified and appalled her. She knew she must break the engagement.

'I don't understand you, Jan,' Angela said. 'Don't you love Daryl? I thought you were as much in love with him as I am with Pete?'

'In a way, I am – but I suppose not enough to marry him,' was Jeanette's evasive reply.

On their next date, she returned Daryl's ring. His disappointment momentarily saddened her and even made her feel a little guilty, but overriding any other emotion was her relief at being free from her commitment. She knew now for a certainty that she did not want ever to be married – or to have children. She would concentrate on something she really did want and which held no fears for her. She would become a nurse.

17

Even without being told so by the other girls, she realised that her chances of success were slim. She was still without qualifications of any kind despite the knowledge she had been storing up in her mind for the past year and a half. The matron of the hospital told her that she had done very well as an auxiliary but, in the same conversation, warned Jeanette that her aloofness and unwillingness to communicate with the other staff were not in her favour. She was not, in matron's assessment, a good mixer and since so much of hospital life involved teamwork, this would count against her.

Jeanette accepted the criticism as fair, but her emotional withdrawal into her own private world was no longer within her control. To explain her thoughts and feelings to anyone was totally abhorrent and she could not do it.

Nevertheless, her verbal inarticulateness did not hinder the sharp perceptions of her mind. She entered a competition sponsored by Sir Archibald McIndoe in which the young nurses were invited to write their views of the work that was being done in his unit.

Like all the staff, Jeanette was a keen admirer of the great surgeon and his technical skill. But, unlike them, she considered there were many faults in the management of the unit. Patients, she felt, were treated almost as if they were cogs in the wheel of the hospital. They were numbers rather than individuals. Their treatment seemed to Jeanette to ignore them as people, their deep-rooted fears about their futures; with frightening inferiority complexes induced by the sight of their mutilated faces and bodies in a mirror; with bouts of terrible – sometimes suicidal – despair. Jeanette believed that it was not just their burned skins which needed attention but, scarred as they were by their accidents, their minds too. The present system appeared to her to leave them too exposed and vulnerable. She put her thoughts frankly and succinctly into her thesis and handed in her entry with a mixture of defiance and satisfaction that she had had this unexpected opportunity to declare her views.

'How could you dare write all that?' said Angela. 'We're not even proper nurses and you've actually criticised the Great Man's holy of holies. You're sure to get chucked out. Whatever made you do it!'

A little of Jeanette's euphoria evaporated as she viewed the enormity of what she had done. Her only hope of being considered by any hospital for nursing training was to have an exceptionally good recommendation from this one. Angela was right – she must have been mad. Jeanette, as well as her contemporaries, had under-estimated the stature of the man. She won the competition.

For the first time in her life, Jeanette felt a sense of achievement. Thus stimulated, she set about writing to various hospitals with a view to sitting their entrance exams. Most of all, she wanted to go to Carshalton in Surrey where her grandmother was now living. She was granted an interview – her first – with the nursing tutor. It did not last long. Looking at the tall ungainly girl facing her, the woman said with ill-concealed impatience:

'You don't even have *one* 'O'-level, Miss Roberts. You must realise that nursing is not simply a matter of caring for patients. You have to be able to write intelligent, coherent reports; you have to be able to understand the type and quantity of the drugs you will be administering. You have to be able to fill in graphs; take written as well as oral exams. I'm sorry. I see you have excellent references from your Dr Barnado's employers, and the matron at the Queen Vic. But believe me – *no nursing school will take you*. My advice to you is to look for some allied career in a field where you do not need academic qualifications.'

Tight-lipped, Jeanette returned to East Grinstead.

'What will you do now?' Angela asked, her voice sympathetic.

'Apply elsewhere,' Jeanette said curtly. 'I'm going to be a nurse – and that's all there is to it. I'll get in somehow – somewhere.'

Jeanette had other interviews, equally negative.

'It is not your fault, my dear, but you simply don't come from the right sort of background. You are wasting your time,' one of the tutors commented. There was no kind way by which she could tell this gauche girl with her awkward manner and poor diction that at best she might make the grade as a ward orderly.

Jeanette felt no self-pity – only anger. She *knew* she could be a good nurse if only she could be given the chance to prove it.

19

'I'm not giving up,' she said furiously to Angela.

A few months later, Jeanette saw an advertisement in a nursing magazine stating that the entrance examination for the Mile End Hospital in the East End could be taken without academic qualifications. Jeanette applied immediately, convinced that she would scrape through the exam. She could read, she could write and her memory for all she had learned as an auxiliary nurse was nearly faultless: why should she fail?

Jeanette read the examination paper with a sense of dismay as total as her previous conviction. In many instances, she could not even understand the maths questions, let alone contemplate answering them. Her heart and her hopes sank. She glanced round the room where eight other girls, aged nineteen or twenty, were already beginning to write on their exam sheets. She knew from the invigilator's instructions that she could not leave the room until the allotted time had passed. Her eyes went to the blank sheet of paper in front of her. It seemed to be crying out for something to be written on it.

Suddenly Jeanette was consumed with a familiar anger at the injustice of the world. No one had told her all those years ago that one day she would need the facts the teachers were trying to get across to her. She had had no reason then to want to learn. She would learn now if only they would allow her to. At the end of the day, why were academic qualifications so important? Surely it mattered far more that you should be dependable, efficient, reliable; that you could keep your head in a crisis and not panic.

Almost without thinking, her hand reached for her fountain pen. She would put something on that blank sheet. She would tell them that this was no way to select their nursing candidates since their methods excluded someone such as herself who longed to dedicate her life to nursing. Their exam, she wrote furiously, was no more than a test to discover who would come top of the form at school . . . and what had that to do with life in a hospital? Would the answer to a long-division sum help to make someone well, ease someone's pain, comfort a sick child? Would multiplication help you deliver a baby, give first aid to a patient? Would the ability to spell help you keep calm in a crisis?

Jeanette wrote . . . and wrote, and when finally she laid down her pen, her wrist ached. She was certain there were innumerable spelling mistakes but she didn't care. She had said what needed to be said, and besides, what did it matter? With not one single question answered, she must inevitably fail the exam.

That night, when she returned to the nurses' home at East Grinstead, Angela viewed her pale taut face anxiously.

'Didn't it go well, Jan?' she asked tentatively.

There was a burning sensation behind Jeanette's eyes but she did not cry. She had not cried since she was eleven years old. Perhaps she could no longer shed tears.

'No, it didn't go well!' she said in a small tight voice. 'It didn't go at all if you want the truth . . .' There was an ironic twist to her mouth as she shrugged her shoulders with pretended indifference. 'Forget it, Angela. I couldn't answer one single question. Obviously I've failed.'

Chapter 3

'Tower Hamlets is probably the most deprived Borough in Inner London . . . with 18,000 children between 5 and 14. Over half qualify for free school meals, over half leave school with no qualifications, 42% of their parents are unemployed (London average 19%), over a quarter are one-parent families. Tower Hamlets has the highest number of recorded racial attacks and mortality rate in London. In November 1986 the number of child abuse cases was reported as being a "staggering three times the national average".'
(Bob Le Vaillant, Director, Stepney Children's Fund, Toynbee Hall Children and Families with Special Needs Department)

The Mile End Hospital panel assessing the examination papers were impressed by Jeanette's impassioned outcry and decided to give her a trial.

Within a few days of starting the career she had wanted so desperately, Jeanette realised the full extent of the gaps in her academic education. But the young girl's grim determination to make up for this backlog impressed the tutor, Miss Graham, who sensed that Jeanette had the strength of character to overcome her handicaps. She began by spending whatever time she could spare teaching the girl the basics of simple mathematics and English grammar.

'Knowing how little you know is the first step to knowledge,' she told Jeanette with a smile. 'You've made a good start!'

In later years, Jeanette was the first to admit that she would never have passed even the preliminary nursing exams but for the help of this particular tutor.

Every morning she rose at five o'clock in order to put in a few hours study before classes began at eight. At night, whilst the other student nurses were out enjoying themselves, she was to be found in the library. Her presence there, sometimes until one or two in the morning, became so commonplace that eventually the librarian gave Jeanette the key when she went off duty, leaving her to lock up. If Jeanette was not in her room in the Nurses' Home or in the library, she would be in Miss Graham's office receiving tuition.

Both her tutor and one of the nursing sisters were dedicated Christians, and tried to interest the lone silent girl in their beliefs. But since during those long years of single-minded work Jeanette could see no worthwhile connection between spiritual matters and her single objective to pass her exams, she resisted any attempts to interest her in some mythical 'higher purpose' controlling her destiny. Now, for the first time she felt she was in control and she could not afford any diversions.

Her life seemed to have entered an easier phase. Her mother had married again. Dan and four of her new husband's six children lived with them. Their council house in Bromley was noisy and overcrowded. It lacked any luxuries, but to Jeanette's relief it also lacked the violent undertones of her childhood experiences.

She revealed little of her personal life to her tutor, nor indeed to any of the young student nurses who tried to befriend her. Although she realised that she was looked upon by everyone with whom she came in contact as an anomalous oddity, a loner, she did not care. To qualify as a fully trained nurse was all she asked of life – and this, bit by bit, she achieved, passing all the exams at her first attempt. She was intensely glad, not only for herself, but because each pass-mark vindicated her tutor's faith in her.

But those three long years of intense hard work following upon her childhood of deprivation took their toll on Jeanette's physical health. Shortly after she qualified, she was admitted to the hospital seriously ill with acute anaemia and bacterial endocarditis. For a while her recovery was in question, but the doctors had underestimated her willpower. Jeanette was not prepared to die just when she had finally achieved her ambition to become a nurse. She struggled slowly back to health and, as soon as she was fit enough, threw herself into her work as a staff nurse, gaining experience during the subsequent four years in children's nursing and completing her midwifery course.

It was during Jeanette's training that two of her fellow students, Rose and Maggie, became friendly with her. Although they did not understand why Jeanette was so uncommunicative, they liked and respected her. Having themselves decided to join a Nursing Association where they hoped to be able to do worthwhile work as District Nurses in a deprived area of East London, they invited Jeanette to go with them. Since it did not concern her where she worked provided she was nursing, Jeanette asked the only question that mattered to her.

'Can I live in? If so, I'll join the Association with you.'

She had no idea then what the work would entail. Some of the big tower blocks and surrounding streets were crammed with the poor, the unemployed, the helpless and the hopeless. There, Jeanette met families with neglected, often starving children; with babies as often as not unwanted, born into unhygienic overcrowded flats; women with bruised faces and bodies, whose husbands drank away what little income there was in the hope of forgetting the degradation of their present lives and their hopelessness for their future. There was so much Jeanette could do – so much that needed to be done, that she found the work more than rewarding.

But her spirit was not entirely at rest. She found herself becoming increasingly curious about the Christian doctrines which seemed to be a particular source of strength and comfort to her former tutor, Miss Graham, and to so many of her fellow nurses. She had no wish to become involved with their Baptist meetings and Bible classes, and yet envied them the certainty of their convictions. She also admired their courage for they quite openly acknowledged their beliefs despite the disapproval of Baptists shown by certain members of the staff. Although the nurses' attendance at Bible meetings was never forbidden, they warned Jeanette that her association with them would not be looked on with favour.

'It's a risk we all take,' one of her new friends, Joyce Nash, explained. 'I think it is our spiritual strength which frightens those who are less secure. But do watch your step, Jeanette! Girls have been turfed out on the flimsiest of pretexts.'

The spirit of rebellion, which never lay far from the surface of Jeanette's emotions, began to simmer. Despite her genuine fear of expulsion, she allowed herself to be taught the Christian doctrines. She discovered much in their belief in the intrinsic value of every single human being that answered her own need to be valued. Like all battered or abused children, she had a desperately low opinion of herself which had not been lessened by her recent academic achievements. She wanted – needed – to believe that someone, albeit a mythical God, had put her in this world for a purpose and actually cared about her as a person.

Joyce introduced her to a young couple with five children who invited her to their home. It was the first time that Jeanette saw a family home so filled with love that it extended even to herself, a comparative stranger. She met also a group of Christian nurses who invited her to holiday with them in Cornwall.

Jeanette returned from that holiday determined to become a Christian. For the first time since she was eleven years old, she felt a complete person – free, if not from all the anger and bitterness that she had lived with for so long, at least from a large part of it. There seemed little point in postponing the inevitable scene she knew would ensue when she told her superiors. She marched straight in and declared her intent. Jeanette herself was in no doubt that the reason for her subsequent expulsion was because she had aligned herself with her friends; if there were other reasons she was not given them. Forty-eight hours later, she found herself without a job and, therefore, without a roof over her head.

Despite the efforts of the other nurses to have Jeanette reinstated – even the Governors were approached – the dictatorial decision was upheld. Furthermore, the reference she was given made her applications elsewhere a hopeless task. She tried not to feel bitter, not only about the injustice of the situation, but about this new God for whom she had risked her career and who was repaying her allegiance in such a cruel and negative fashion! Jeanette's old hatred for humanity returned, threatening once more to overwhelm her.

She found a bed-sit and finally obtained work in a factory as an industrial nurse. She kept in touch with her friends and was persuaded by them to continue to attend their meetings and Bible classes. She was now nearing thirty, but there were times when she felt ninety. Unknown to her, she was suffering from an acute kidney infection and gradually, as her health failed, she became almost too ill to carry out her work.

It was her friend, Joyce Nash, now a District Nurse, who, meeting her one day after work, recognised the symptoms of kidney infection and took her straight back to her own home and put her to bed. The doctor said that since nothing would be gained by hospital treatment and Joyce was qualified to take care of her, Jeanette could remain in her friend's home.

Her recovery was slow, but the moment she was fit enough to return to her tiny one-bedroomed flat in Poplar and to her job in the factory, Jeanette did so. Despite the fact that she liked Joyce and was immensely grateful to her for her care and hospitality, she was still basically a loner. She still retained the belief that she was a lesser being whose true self was best left undiscovered by those she liked and admired.

Her Christian friends respected this obvious barrier to intimacy, yet were puzzled and often hurt by it. Knowing little or nothing of Jeanette's childhood, still less of the emotional damage it had caused, they were confused, but refused to be offended by her off-hand manner.

Jeanette's new way of life, devoid as it was of any real social outlet, seemed set in its pattern of work. She managed to maintain her flat on her meagre salary and to find money for petrol for occasional weekend visits to her mother, or to Betsy. Her sister was now married and living in Kent. Less frequently, she saw Alan and his wife who now had a young family.

The pattern of Jeanette's existence was limited by lack of time and money. But as she set off one summer evening to do her shopping at the local Woolworth store she often frequented, a chance meeting with a child was to bring about a radical, far-reaching change in her life.

As she passed the sweet counter, her eye was caught by the sight of a small boy surreptitiously helping himself to a bag of sweets. He looked like so many of the urchins who frequented the streets of London's East End – dirty, unkempt, his jersey pitted with unmended holes, his shoes two sizes too large, his face painfully thin beneath the grime and, she noted with her trained eye, showed signs of bruising. His eyes, furtive and calculating, met hers briefly before he turned to run.

Jeanette was overcome by conflicting emotions. There had been many times in her childhood when she had often stolen food and sweets. The boy was too young to attend a juvenile court, so nothing would be achieved by reporting him – he would still be hungry and he would not stop stealing. Better that she should take him back to his home and try to make his parents understand that if he were not to grow up delinquent, he *must* have proper care. He was little more than five years old, sickly with the pallor of the malnourished.

As she grabbed his arm she felt the toe of his shoe kick sharply at her ankle. He tried to twist his pathetically thin arm free from her restraining grip.

'Lemme go, you silly bitch...' The profanities which now poured from the young child's lips did not shock or surprise Jeanette; but those people standing near enough to see and hear were growing curious. Hurriedly she replaced the stolen bag of sweets and dragged the child out into the street.

There was a faint look of surprise on his face as his struggles slowly ceased.

'Ain'tcha gonna turn me in?' he asked.

'No, I'm not, but don't think you're getting off scot-free,' Jeanette said firmly. 'I'm taking you home – to your home. What's your name and where do you live?'

Momentarily his face went blank – deliberately so.

'I can find out for myself,' Jeanette said calmly, 'but it'll save time if you tell me.'

'Ain't nobody there,' the boy muttered after a moment's hesitation.

'Then we'll wait till someone gets home.' Jeanette said.

27

She kept her hold on him as he led the way through a series of back streets to the dingy row of terraced houses where, apparently, he lived. Refuse littered the basement areas round the houses and the gutters were filled with dirty scraps of paper, rotting cardboard, and fly-blown garbage. Occasionally a face peered out at them from behind curtains discoloured by dirt and age. Neighbours! Jeanette thought with a surge of her old hatred. How she had hated their watchful curious eyes.

'When's your Dad get back from work Robbie?' she asked, glancing at her watch. 'You said Robbie, didn't you? – because I'm waiting here till he comes home.'

'Ain't got no Dad – 'e scarpered years ago!'

'Your Mum then – when does she get back?'

The boy shrugged.

'Gone ter Bingo,' he said briefly.

'But when will she be back?'

He did not trouble to reply but shrugged his shoulders indicatively.

'Then we'll wait here,' Jeanette said seating herself on the wall. Someone must return soon. Almost certainly there would be other children.

She continued to wait with the now silent child beside her as hour after hour went by. Stubbornly she refused to abandon her vigil. Eventually a small girl came down the street towards them, pushing a toddler in an old pram.

'Me sister, Joan,' Robbie announced. 'The little 'un's me uvver sister, Crissie.'

His greeting to his sister was brief. 'I'm 'ungry!' he announced but without a real expectation of relief in his voice.

The nine-year-old girl shrugged.

'So'm I!' she said, glancing at Jeanette without curiosity. She joined them on the wall, moving only once to shove a dummy into the toddler's mouth when the infant began to wail.

'Yells if she don' 'ave it' she informed Jeanette, indifferent to the reason for this strange woman's presence outside her house.

It was beginning to get dark and very cold before they were joined by one of Robbie's three older brothers.

'Two of 'em bash us one if we get in their way,' Joan explained with simple truth. 'This one's Frank. 'E don' 'it us.'

The new arrival glanced silently at the group, but like his sister, did not question Jeanette's presence any more than he questioned the reason for his mother's late return home. The visits to the Bingo hall were a regular state of affairs.

'What do you do with yourselves when your Mum's out?' Jeanette asked curiously. 'Do you go to the youth club?'

Frank grinned, his thin adolescent face momentarily attractive as he raised his eyebrows laconically.

'Got chucked out!' he admitted. 'Said we're trouble. Nicked fings – yer know...' he added vaguely.

'Me too' Robbie added. 'An' me mate Tom. 'Im and me 'cos we was bustin' winders.'

'So you've nowhere to go now,' Jeanette said more to herself than to the children.

'Didn' like it neither,' Frank said. 'Can't swear nor nuffink. We was always gettin' told off.'

Not only did they hate the clubs which had flung them out but, they went on to tell her, they hated their schools and their homes too. Jeanette was the first grown up they'd come across who was in the least interested in what they thought or did.

'Maybe I could find somewhere for us to meet – when you've nothing better to do.' Jeanette said impulsively. 'We could talk, play games. I could read the younger ones stories from the Bible. It doesn't bother me if you swear but if we do get our own club together, I won't have it vandalised. It'd be our place – your place – and I'd expect you kids to look after it.'

'Cor! Be smashin'!' was Robbie's altogether appropriate reply.

It was near midnight before the children's mother returned. She had failed to win any prizes at Bingo and, judging by her expression, she was in a bad mood. She didn't care that Jeanette had caught her youngest son thieving. It wasn't her fault there wasn't enough money to keep all six of her kids fed and clothed, she complained as she unlocked the front door. How was she expected to manage on the money she got without a man to bring in a decent wage? Trust a man to walk out when the going got tough. How could anyone expect her to keep the kids out of trouble – a woman by herself? It wasn't right to expect it of her. She'd always been unlucky – ever since she'd been a kid.

'I'm starvin', Mum!' Robbie's childish treble broke on on the woman's monologue.

'Oh, shut up with your bloody moanin'!' his mother said harshly, but she did not strike the boy as Jeanette had half expected.

'Watcha gonna do?' she asked Jeanette, her tone signifying her indifference. 'Turn 'im in? Stupid little bastard!' she added, pushing Robbie aside as she headed towards the kitchen.

Jeanette shook her head.

'No! But if you don't watch out for him, he'll end up in trouble anyway. Now, I'm sure he'd like his tea.'

'Bloody bonkers – that's what you are!' the woman said, as she went over to the breadbin.

Robbie's eyes focussed on Jeanette with something akin to gratitude in his expression. Here at last was someone who understood his need.

'Gonna 'ave food at your club?' he asked bluntly. 'You got food, I'll come. I don't mind listenin' to yer ol' Bible stories – not if yer got sumpin to eat! Me mate Tom, 'e'll come too.'

Despite his mother's attempt to persuade Jeanette to stay 'for a cuppa and a chat', she chose to leave. It was late and she had to be up early the next day.

The following evening, Jeanette went down to the Church Housing Association to whom she had applied for a flat. Did they, she enquired, know of any room or hall where she could form a club for some needy children?

'We've nothing to offer you but you could try Alex Mackee, the London City Missioner,' she was told.

To her surprise, not only was the Missioner welcoming, inviting her in to have a cup of tea with him, but he was also sympathetic to her plan to keep the children off the streets at night. Without further hesitation, he offered her the use of his Mission Hall.

Alex Mackee's unquestioning acceptance of, and faith in, Jeanette's ability to benefit the children gave her a new confidence in herself. She went that same week to Robbie's home and told him he could bring as many of his family and friends as he wished to their first club meeting on the following Wednesday.

She had no idea as she walked home that she was to open the door of the Mission Hall not just to a dozen or so children with nowhere else to go, but to fifty, sixty, seventy of them. There were too many even that first day for her to count. Like Robbie and his brother and elder sister, all had been thrown out of youth clubs for disruptive behaviour. These juvenile victims of an uncaring society were all exactly as she had once been, Jeanette thought.

Someone had to care, she decided as she set about organising them – even if it was only for a few hours on a Wednesday night. If there had been someone to understand her needs, she might have been spared untold misery and emotional deprivation. Somehow she was going to make each child aware that *she* cared.

Jeanette did not realise it then, but a life-long commitment had begun.

Chapter 4

'In reaching any decision relating to a child in its care, a local authority shall give first consideration to safeguard and promote the welfare of the child throughout his childhood. And, so far as is practicable, ascertain the wishes and feelings of the child...' Childrens Act 1948. Child Care Act 1980.
(H. Tunnicliffe, The Law Says..., Pepar Publications, 1985)

Although Jeanette had once more obtained full-time employment as an Occupational Health Nurse, money was desperately short. The added expense of maintaining her new flat left little over to support her Wednesday club for the children. Her friend, Joyce, and some of the other nurses contributed what little they could to pay for the lemonade, biscuits and various pieces of equipment Jeanette needed.

As the months went by, the numbers attending the Bible Club greatly increased. With the assistance of Joyce, some nursing friends, a schoolteacher and friends from the local Baptist church, they divided the children into age groups and opened two further clubs. Jeanette called a meeting of the older children and openly discussed with them the problems of financing their enterprise. The children themselves opted to pay a contribution of sixpence a week with those unable to pay being subsidised surreptitiously by Jeanette or Joyce.

They were their clubs, Jeanette insisted, and all decisions would be democratically agreed by majority vote. Astonishingly, there was no vandalism and no thieving. The numbers increased as word spread that there was a place to go where they would be accepted; where they could enjoy a brief respite from the stressful conditions existing in nearly all their homes.

But Jeanette had started a ball rolling which now rapidly gathered speed. Not only Robbie but Tom, his three-year-old friend, had asked if they could stay overnight at Jeanette's flat, Robbie because he said he was being beaten by an older brother, Tom because he would be warm and would receive some attention to his needs. From enquiries Jeanette made, she learned that the younger boy's family was registered as being one of the most needy in the area. Not only had a baby died in unexplained circumstances, but one of Tom's older brothers was already in psychiatric care, and his sister, Cathy, who often escorted him to Jeanette's flat, was scheduled to attend the same unit when a place could be found for her.

Somehow, Jeanette made room for the two boys, but before long there were as many as ten children seeking refuge with her at weekends. But for the fact that they were at school and she was working, Jeanette might have had them during the week as well. She gave each of them a small suitcase or bag in which they could keep their few private treasures: a painting which had been praised at school, a toy, an article of clothing.

Joyce came as often as she could spare the time to assist. There was no lack of work. The children would arrive at the flat on a Friday evening, some riddled with lice and fleas. A set of clothes was bought for each of them from jumble stalls and Oxfam shops and, after a disinfecting bath, they changed into these clean clothes. Joyce or Jeanette would take their discarded ones, often lousy and stinking from dirt and urine, to the nearest laundrette. The clean clothes would be donned once more by the children on a Sunday evening.

Joyce, who was still living happily with her widowed mother in a respectable, conventional and loving home, felt morally obliged to help Jeanette in her struggle to help these deprived and often battered children. She was now contributing ten pounds a week from her wages to help feed, clothe and maintain the children, and Jeanette contributed whatever she could spare from her limited budget.

33

'Jeanette must have a great fund of maternal love in her,' one of the nurses remarked to Joyce. 'You at least have a social life, but for her, it's nothing but work and the kids, and not a penny spent on herself.'

'Love!' Jeanette exclaimed when Joyce repeated the remark. 'If you want the truth, I can't even find the kids likeable. Their habits are appalling – not that they can help it, poor little tykes.'

It was the indiscriminate places in which they urinated that made life so difficult. Inevitably they wet their beds, but in addition, some of the younger ones would climb out of bed and urinate where they stood, soaking the carpet, their clothes; or up against a wall, in the sink.

She sensed that it was not simply a matter of training they lacked, but the fact that most of them lived in a state of permanent tension and fear. Young Tom, for instance, was scared stiff of his own shadow and she knew she would make no headway in any attempt to toilet train him until this situation changed. It was obvious that the physical violence at home was growing worse and she resolved to go round to his house to talk once more to his mother about it.

'Everyone thinks you're crazy letting the kids come here at weekends,' Joyce said, her eyes taking in the scene in Jeanette's tiny flat – boxes and cardboard containers piled up in the hall, camp beds and sleeping bags shoved into any space available, the minute kitchen piled high with crockery, mugs, extra large cooking pots, supplies of tinned food.

Jeanette could not explain her reasons even to her friend. Her inability to refuse shelter to one of these neglected children lay somewhere in her own past. The system for bringing relief or succour had failed her and now, twenty years later, it was failing them. Each child must return home after the weekend respite to repeated family abuse, violence and disorder. Each reappeared the following weekend with new cuts, bruises, welts – dirty, hungry and frightened. It seemed there was no one who cared other than herself, her various nursing friends who volunteered some of their time to help her and a schoolteacher who played the piano for the Bible sing-songs – a pastime the children really enjoyed.

*

34

It was not only at weekends that Jeanette's flat was occupied. Robbie, for one, frequently ran away from home and she would find him waiting outside her door when she returned from work. Despite the livid marks on his face and body from the latest confrontation he had had with his brothers, he never cried. Had she not seen him wince when she accidentally touched a bruise, she might have thought he felt no pain. Jeanette treated his injuries as best she could, recognising his inability to cry as a withdrawal from the acknowledgement of pain – something she, too, had achieved when she was a child.

The boy seemed to have adopted her flat as his second home and it was Jeanette's address he gave one night when caught by the police.

Jeanette was on night duty when the phone rang.

'Mrs Roberts? You'd better come down right away to the station. We have your son here and he's in very serious trouble.'

'I don't have a son – and I'm Miss not Mrs,' Jeanette answered.

'Well, the lad insists you're his mother. Says his name is Robbie. We want you down here right away. The boy's drunk!'

Jeanette went down to the police station. Robbie, now aged six, was indeed very drunk. He was being violently sick.

Jeanette explained her connection with the child and whilst a sergeant went off to fetch Robbie's mother, she learned what had happened. Earlier that night Robbie had been forced by his older brothers to go with them to a wine bottling factory: being so tiny, he was the obvious means of entry into the building via a small skylight. Once inside, it was his task to hand out the bottles of wine to his brothers. When they had as many as they could carry, the older boys ran off, leaving him alone. He had started to drink from a bottle his brothers had left behind and, liking the taste, had finished the lot before a passing police constable found him.

'I'll kill the little bugger!' Robbie's mother shouted when finally she arrived. She turned to Jeanette. 'You take him,' she said hysterically. Jeanette realised that Mary was dangerously close to breaking point.

'Okay, I'll take Robbie home with me,' she said quickly. 'Go home, Mary. Sign whatever they want signed and I'll bring him round in the morning before I go to work.'

'You leave him to me' the woman screamed, fear of the consequences of Robbie's escapade heightening her hysteria. 'I'll teach him a lesson he won't forget.'

The threat was no idle one and the police knew it as well as Jeanette. Aware of Jeanette's efforts to keep the local kids off the streets, they opted to release the boy into her care.

It was the first time, but by no means the last, that Jeanette was obliged to stand in for Robbie's mother. Shortly after this incident, she was once more obliged to take on a parental rôle. Not only Robbie and little Tom but a number of other children who were pupils at his primary school had begged Jeanette to attend the school's Open Day for parents. Their own mothers were not interested in their school progress, they told her, and they wanted her there to show the other kids and teachers that *someone* wanted to know how they were getting on. Jeanette could not refuse their pathetic requests.

Shortly after her arrival at the school, one of the teachers approached her.

'Isn't Robbie's mother coming today?' she enquired. 'We particularly want to see her. We wrote and told her so but had no reply. Is she ill?'

Jeanette shook her head, unwilling to voice her firm opinion that Mary was simply indifferent. Tired of battling against impossible odds, she'd given up making any efforts to cope with her children and lived entirely for the brief, spurious excitement she derived from her Bingo sessions.

Jeanette had come to know the unfortunate woman quite well, staying for a cup of tea and a chat whenever she had had to drag a reluctant Robbie home. Lonely and without the support of her own mother, Mary had begun to off-load her worries and complaints.

Jeanette recalled their last meeting – Mary standing in front of the mirror, the toddler, Crissie, playing on the floor. Joan, it seemed, had gone to school. Robbie had a black eye. Mary was outlining her mouth with lipstick with a desperate kind of concentration.

'Off to Bingo in a minute!' she had informed Jeanette unnecessarily.

She'd glanced at her young son with a look of irritation. His eyes stared back at her expressionless.

'Can't stand the way 'e jus' stares at me!' she had commented as if the boy were not there. 'Green eyes – just like 'is father's – rotten- bastard!'

The fact that her husband had walked out and left her with six kids was a source of nagging bitterness.

'They're all the same – men!' she had said, nodding in Crissie's direction. ''Er father didn't want to know when I told 'im he'd got me in the family way. Said it wasn't 'is – but she is. Didn't want to pay maintenance. Now there's six to feed and 'ow the 'ell am I supposed to manage on the measly 'and-out Social Security gives me!'

Satisfied with her appearance, her mood had changed and she had turned to smile briefly at Jeanette.

'Maybe I'll be lucky this afternoon at Bingo. Woman next to me won twenty-five quid last week. I 'aven't won for ages, but I've a feeling I'll be lucky today . . .' She broke off to tip a pile of coins from a milk jug into a cheap plastic handbag and elbowed her way past Robbie. 'Don't just stand there staring!' she had said, frowning once more. 'Get out and find something to do. And wipe your nose, you filthy little tyke!' She picked up the baby and dumped her in the pram blocking the tiny hall-way. 'Me neighbour's keeping an eye on 'er till Joan gets back,' she explained to Jeanette. 'God, who'd want kids! Tie you down morning, noon and night. Bet you're glad you've got none!'

The teacher's voice brought Jeanette's thoughts back to the present.

'It's really very important Robbie's mother should be here,' she was saying earnestly. 'It's about his assessment for his future education. He's to be interviewed by a panel of doctors and teachers.'

Jeanette volunteered to go and find Mary and try to persuade her to come. But despite her efforts, Mary was adamant. She could not return with Jeanette to the school.

'I don't care what they do with 'im,' she said. 'Besides, it won't make no difference what I say – they've made up their minds to send 'im to a special school and that's that. They say the kid can't learn nothing. Born stupid, 'e was. I ain't going – and that's that!'

Jeanette returned to the school, her mind uneasy. It seemed very wrong to her that Robbie should, at the tender age of six, be classified as stupid. He was no more so than she had been at his age.

'Perhaps *you'll* go in and sit with him,' the teacher suggested. 'It's a bit frightening for so young a child to be on his own.'

Half an hour later, Jeanette took Robbie's hand and accompanied him into the room where the school medical officer and several adults were seated. The discussion about Robbie's failure to make any progress during his first year at school began – and then they questioned the child. Beside her, Jeanette felt the boy's body go rigid. His mouth tightened and not a single reply passed his lips.

'The boy's mentally deficient!' the headmistress said as if Robbie could not hear her. 'There's no doubt about it. I endorse my recommendation for him to be sent to a special school.'

'We might consider a place for him in an ESN environment,' one of the others suggested.

'ESN?' Jeanette queried frowning.

'Educationally subnormal!' the headmistress explained. 'But Robbie couldn't cope with that either. He's simply uneducable. In short, Miss Roberts, he needs a place in an institution for the mentally deficient.'

'Mentally deficient!' Jeanette was now on her feet. 'But that's ridiculous – really daft. Robbie's as capable as you or I of learning.'

The row of faces stared back at Jeanette's flushed face disapprovingly. They were unaccustomed to being challenged by the parents.

'Please sit down, Miss Roberts,' the headmistress said coldly. 'I'm sure you mean well but in the first place, you are not even the child's mother and moreover you are hardly qualified to question the judgement of the school medical officer or, indeed, mine. We are professional people and, believe me, I recognise a mentally deficient child when I see one.'

Once more, Jeanette was on her feet. Normally unable to express her feelings verbally, she was now so angry that she was no longer tongue-tied. Words poured from her. Robbie was very far from being a fool. As street-wise as any kid, he knew his way round every alley and street in the neighbourhood – he'd needed to learn this in order to escape from detection when he had been on one of his shop-lifting sprees, she insisted. He'd learned, too, the words of the songs they sang in her Bible class. If he could memorise them, he could memorise the alphabet and multiplication tables. The only reason he'd done so badly at school was because of his background. He hadn't been motivated to learn; he'd played truant so often he'd lost continuity. *Of course* he could learn if he wanted.

One look at the wall of blank faces told Jeanette with a sickening certainty that she might as well have kept her mouth shut. As Robbie's mother had said: 'They've made up their minds and there's nothing I can do about it.'

Well, there was something *she* would do about it, Jeanette thought furiously. She would not allow this to happen – a six-year-old child being put in an institution where he could never hope to learn; condemned to a life amongst genuinely mentally deficient children to whom he could not possibly relate.

'The assessment has been made, Miss Roberts, and it is not our intention to withdraw it.'

'We'll see about that!' Jeanette said, pulling Robbie to his feet, her face white with anger. 'It's you lot who are mentally deficient – not him!'

And she stormed out of the room, dragging the silent child after her.

But Jeanette's mind was uneasy as she returned to her flat. She had not the slightest idea how she could reverse the school's decision.

'I don't think there's anything you *can* do, Jeanette,' Joyce said bluntly. Far better educated than Jeanette, she was familiar with the State school system. 'It's a borough assessment, and like it or not, this is the borough Robbie lives in. It's the system, I'm afraid.'

'Then it's a bloody ridiculous system!' Jeanette said furiously. 'The kid's no fool, Joyce – I'll stake my life on it.'

Later that night, as she lay in bed worrying the problem over and over in her mind, the first faint hope of a solution occurred to her. Her mother now lived in Bromley, where Dan and his stepbrothers and sisters went to school. If she could persuade her mother to accommodate Robbie, perhaps he could be reassessed by a different borough.

On her first free day, Jeanette went to see the headmaster of Dan's school, whom she had met previously when her little brother had started there. He listened sympathetically to her story, but pointed out that there was nothing he could do since the child did not live in his area.

'Even were he to do so, the previous borough assessment would be forwarded to me and I would be obliged to accept it...' He broke off, pausing as a thought crossed his mind. He looked at Jeanette speculatively. 'Of course...' he said slowly, '... if I didn't "know" the situation and if you could find somewhere for the boy to live in this borough, then I might be able to make a place for him here until the official clarification arrived, and that could take three months.' He looked sharply at Jeanette. 'You said the boy was intelligent... but how intelligent, Miss Roberts? You admit he's illiterate. He'd have three months in which to learn the alphabet and write his name. That isn't long – and *you'd* have to teach him. If you succeeded, I'd have grounds to request a reassessment...'

Jeanette's mind worked furiously. How many years was it since she herself had been faced with a similar challenge? Knowing next to nothing, she had only been able to prove that she could qualify as a nurse because Miss Graham was willing to give up her own time to tutor her.

'I'll teach Robbie his alphabet!' she said quietly. 'Thanks for giving him the chance.'

The prospect seemed daunting when she reconsidered it later, but for the time being there were more pressing problems. Her mother agreed to let Robbie live with her, but only provided Jeanette would support the boy. Mary welcomed the deal since there would be one less mouth to feed. Jeanette telephoned the local authority Children's Department and persuaded them to accept an arrangement for Robbie to be listed as a 'Preventative Care' case.

With both hurdles crossed, Jeanette now faced the awesome task of trying to motivate the six-year-old boy to learn. Alerted by the way he peered at a picture book, his head bent so low that his nose almost touched the page, she took him to an optician. He confirmed her suspicion that Robbie's sight was so poor he could barely distinguish shapes, let alone letters. Since he had seen nothing but a blur on the blackboard, it was easy to understand why school had been so meaningless to him.

A week later, she went with Robbie to the dental department of the London Hospital, to which the local G.P. had referred him. Assuming Jeanette was Robbie's mother, the dental surgeon rounded on her with an anger he took no trouble to conceal.

'You are not fit to have this boy in your care,' he stormed, his raised voice so full of fury and disgust that both Jeanette and Robbie flinched. 'The condition of his mouth is appalling... you should be charged with gross neglect... have you no idea of the pain this boy has been enduring... done nothing... affecting his health... your own child... not fit to be a mother...'

The harangue continued, leaving Robbie as well as Jeanette trembling. It was several minutes before finally he paused long enough for her to break in and explain the true situation. Despite the man's whole-hearted apology and the subsequent help he gave Robbie, she prayed that never again would she be submitted to such verbal abuse. Robbie's silent suffering had, she realised, been so acute and for so long part of his life that he had accepted pain as normal. Now, she consoled herself, they could start work in earnest and hopefully he would make the progress necessary to be able to go to the Bromley school.

At first it was not too difficult – the reward of a toy was a sufficient bribe. Jeanette was still working and, indeed, needed the salary she thus earned now she had assumed the extra cost of the boy's keep – but she made time to go down to Bromley most evenings, partly to do Robbie's washing and ironing, but mostly to try to teach him the alphabet. At weekends, she took him back with her to the flat.

Robbie lacked all concentration and his resistance to this call on his free time grew stronger. Understanding nothing of the long-term effects upon his life if he failed to learn, he saw no reason to co-operate with Jeanette and her mother's efforts. He liked both women and was happy in this new, non-violent household where food was comparatively plentiful and he had the other children for company. But *they* did not have to work every hour of the day as he was being made to do. He rebelled.

'I've tried everything!' Jeanette moaned to Joyce. 'Bribery, punishments, threats and – God forgive me – I've lost my temper and shouted at him. It isn't because he can't – it's because he *won't*. I *know* he can learn. Remember how he used to sing the choruses of the Bible songs? He can get most of the alphabet right if we sing it. But at this rate, he'll never say it on his own within the time limit.'

'There's nothing much you can do except keep trying, pushing!' Joyce said practically.

Jeanette grimaced.

'I feel so awful sometimes when I'm shouting at him, I have to leave the room. I know I'm cruel to push him so hard, but Robbie doesn't understand why it matters so much – no more than I did at his age. If it hadn't been for my brother Alan, I'd never would have learned to read and write...'

'You wouldn't yell at him if you didn't believe in your heart that it was the only way to help him', Joyce said, putting a comforting hand on Jeanette's shoulder.

But, as the weeks passed, Robbie's progress seemed so imperceptible as to make Jeanette's goal appear impossible. As he bent his head over the table and wept, she found herself sharing his despair. 'S'no good, Jeanette,' he wailed. 'I ain't never *ever* gonna learn.'

Chapter 5

'A social worker being criticised for not picking up a potential case of battering in time, may be a young trainee... (only approximately 30% are fully trained)... or an experienced senior whose case-load of 140 clients made daily visits impossible.'
(Jean Renvoize, Children in Danger, *Routledge & Kegan Paul, 1974)*

As Jeanette watched the woman opposite her leafing through the document she was holding, she reflected that it must be all of two years since she and Robbie had last seen her. They had been difficult years. From the first, he had continued to steal, to run away, to throw temper tantrums, and was entirely lacking in even the most basic of social graces. Jeanette had made a conscious decision not to attempt disciplining him, realising that if she were to put too much pressure on the child, he would opt out of co-operating with the efforts to educate him. Although she always told Robbie when his behaviour was unacceptable, she never tried to enforce a change. Even after two years, he could still not bear any physical contact and if an attempt were made to hold his hand, would quickly withdraw it.

Despite the ever present shortage of time at her disposal, Jeanette had continued to take the boy every Friday night to visit his mother. Whatever a child's feelings were towards their natural parents, she believed it was important that contact should continue, and she herself did her utmost to maintain a

43

friendly relationship with them. It was a policy she was to continue in later years with every child who came into her care. Whenever possible she would point out to a child the parent's good points; stress that there were reasons for their failure to be the kind of mother or father the child wanted; that they must try to take a compassionate view of them and accept them as they were – in the same way that *she* accepted each child regardless of any faults he or she might have. She knew that to destroy or diminish a relationship between a child and its natural parents might harm them in the future, especially were they to return home at a later stage of their lives.

Jeanette was still bearing the entire cost of feeding and clothing Robbie, but despite the financial worries, she considered the struggle to educate him had been more than worthwhile. By the end of the three-months allowed, he had finally mastered the alphabet, and he could even write his name. True to his promise, the kindly headmaster had taken him on at the local school. When eventually the borough assessment had caught up with Robbie, he had continually to be tested to see if he could maintain the progress he was making. Now, at long last, Jeanette had won her battle to have the boy reassessed, and they were sitting in the same school where, two years previously, the same panel had pronounced him uneducable.

The woman facing Jeanette laid down Robbie's documents.

'I'm afraid we have the wrong file here!' she said. 'There's been a mistake. We're supposed to be reviewing Robbie Jackson aged eight, are we not?'

'This boy's headmaster says here that he is well up with his age-group... intelligent and...' She broke off, her face suffusing with a dark flush of embarrassment as suddenly she recognised Jeanette. She passed the file to one of her colleagues. After a moment's silence, she said awkwardly: 'It would seem as if we have made a serious misjudgement! You were quite right about the child... Miss Roberts, isn't it?... I owe you an apology.'

But now anger and an underlying bitterness at a system which could so nearly have ruined a child's life gave Jeanette the courage to speak out.

'No, you don't owe me an apology,' she replied rudely. 'You

44

owe it to Robbie. It was *his* life you nearly ruined.'

She had no regrets as she took Robbie back to her tiny, overcrowded flat. Joyce came in that evening to share Jeanette's day of triumph. She felt humbled by her friend's determination and selflessness, and decided the time had come for her to voice her growing compulsion to become involved in a more positive way. Knowing her commitment could not be a casual one, she had struggled for over a year against the conviction that she must devote more of her time and herself to helping Jeanette. She realised that she would have to sacrifice many other interests. At the age of thirty-three, she had relinquished the hope of a conventional marriage and children of her own. Yet stability in the lives of the children was one of Jeanette's prime objectives and Joyce accepted that it could only be harmful if her involvement was suddenly to cease because she had found a better or more satisfying future. Now, despite all the reasons she gave herself for remaining at arm's length from Jeanette's enterprise, she knew she could not continue to do so.

'I've been thinking,' she said. 'You can't go on coping in this tiny flat, Jeanette. What about me sharing the rent of a bigger place? I've just been playing the "aunt" at weekends and doling out a bit of cash from time to time. I'd like to be more involved. Will you think about it?'

Until this point in their lives, neither of the two young women had consciously planned a working partnership; they had had little in common beyond their shared belief in the Christian doctrine. Their present relationship had evolved by degrees as they had worked together to help the children Jeanette had taken under her wing. Each had come to appreciate the other's contribution. Joyce was constantly surprised and impressed by Jeanette's ability always to see to the heart of a child's problems and, somehow, to find a way to deal with them. Joyce was able sometimes to point out to Jeanette that she was wrong in supposing there was an underlying psychological reason why one of the children was behaving unreasonably; that indeed such behaviour was typical of any child reacting against discipline, affected by developing adolescence, denied what they wanted.

They now realised that quite by chance, they perfectly

complemented one another. Their friendship had the added advantage of being impersonal, although there were to be occasions when Joyce would be distressed and irritated by Jeanette's habit of taking an argument as a personal affront. Not yet free of her ingrained inferiority complex, Jeanette was inclined to misconstrue a remark that her viewpoint was 'a silly one' as being a criticism that she herself was silly. This was one of many adjustments they would both have to make.

Their emotional separateness was to have many more advantages than either foresaw at this moment as they sat discussing the possibility of sharing a home. They were to be linked in friendship and partnership, but because of their individuality, the children could never – as most children do and foster children in particular – try to play one off against the other or put a wedge between them as they might have done with parents. A married couple had their relationship with each other to manage at a time when their child might be presenting additional problems. Joyce and Jeanette were to have no such distraction.

Jeanette realised that Joyce's suggestion would afford a perfect solution to the immense problem of overcrowding that took place every weekend. She started looking for more spacious accommodation, but before she found a suitable flat to move into, she received a telephone call from the Family Service Unit. Her work with the children of the neighbourhood had become known to the various welfare authorities as had her miraculous achievement with Robbie.

'It's about Cathy MacPhearson!' the voice on the other end of the telephone informed Jeanette. 'I know you often look after her younger brother, Tom. Now we've got to find temporary care for the girl. She's been expelled from school and her mother can't cope. It's only for three weeks, Jeanette – then we hope to get her into a psychiatric unit. We'll pay for her keep – and, of course, for any damage she does. She's rather violent...'

Jeanette had already come to know Cathy well through the Bible Club. Moreover it was usually Cathy who brought her seven-year-old younger brother, Tom, round to the flat when a violent scene was going on at home.

'It's only for three weeks!' the voice continued persuasively.

46

'The thing is, we can't find anywhere else to send her – not with her record.'

Accustomed as Jeanette was to the periodic outbursts of violence from the emotionally disturbed children who came to her flat, her familiarity with this type of behaviour did little to lessen the shock of the fourteen-year-old girl's disruptiveness. Windows were smashed, chairs broken, curtains ripped to shreds and Jeanette herself attacked when Cathy flew into one of her rages at the slightest attempt to discipline her. Already sexually aware, she wanted to spend her time down at the building site where she knew the men would laugh at her, encourage her to flaunt herself and call out lewd suggestions whose meanings she perfectly well understood. Jeanette knew it was only a matter of time before one of them took advantage of the girl's blatant behaviour, if they had not already done so. There was no alternative but to confine her to her room.

On a matter of principle, Jeanette would never lock a door. She could command obedience merely by talking to a child, reiterating firmly, but quietly, that since he or she was living in her house, they must obey her rules. Those rules she made were as few as possible, but she insisted upon them with a determination which left the child in no doubt she expected their compliance. She did not punish every breach of conduct, but found time to talk quietly to the culprit.

With Cathy – as with so many of the children – Jeanette had long since established a relationship, the basis of which was that Cathy was aware that she cared for and about her. For Cathy to go against her wishes, Jeanette reasoned with her, was to show how little *she* cared about Jeanette. Was that what she wanted?

Cathy was tall for her age, long-limbed and statuesque in build. She might have been considered pretty but her appearance was very far from prepossessing. Her brown hair was unbrushed and in wild, unkempt tangles. She wore men's clothing several sizes too large for her and her posture and movements were that of an ungainly tomboy, lacking any feminine grace. She never smiled and her expression was truculent and defensive.

Cathy did not run away. She had other methods by which she indicated the depths of her inability to cope with the only life she had known for the past fourteen years, with her despair and

47

rebellion and with her need for Jeanette's attention. Jeanette would find Cathy's faeces hidden in her coat pocket, stuffed behind in a panel in the bathroom or jamming up the lavatory cistern. Even more distressingly, Jeanette would discover used sanitary towels deliberately placed in her handbag, where she would come upon them unexpectedly – perhaps in shop or on a bus. These actions were, Jeanette realised, all indications of the degree of the girl's disturbance.

'Thank the good Lord it's only for three weeks!' was Joyce's cheerful comment as she came upon Jeanette struggling to restrain Cathy, who, during one of her violent tantrums, had yet again broken a window, showering the sitting-room floor with glass. But the three weeks became four, then a month, then two months, as still her social worker was unable to obtain a place for her in the psychiatric unit.

It had quickly become obvious to Jeanette that the girl could not be left alone in the flat whilst she herself was at work. Fortunately, her mother was once again willing to take a weekly boarder. Jeanette provided the wherewithal for Cathy's keep. Mrs Jevons had proved a caring and conscientious guardian for Robbie, and children generally seemed to like her. Since her remarriage, she had quickly become popular in and around the council estate where she lived and was known as a friendly, generous and obliging woman to her neighbours.

Sadly, it seemed to Jeanette that her relationship with her mother was little more than a working partnership; that she was still blamed for the breakdown of her parents' marriage. The past was never discussed and the rift between them seemed irreconcilable. There were no birthday presents – not even a birthday card, although her mother never forgot to send one to Joyce, whose birthday fell on the same day. She never proffered a word of praise to Jeanette for her achievement in becoming a fully qualified nurse; nor encouragement for the work she was doing with the children in her neighbourhood, although she praised her to others and was always willing to help if she could, visiting Jeanette's flat when another pair of hands was needed; or, as she often did, by making toys or knitting for the local children. Her mother's attitude hurt Jeanette deeply, but she hoped that time would eventually bring them closer.

Meanwhile she appreciated her willingness to cope with a difficult child like Cathy.

Since Cathy came home every weekend, the move to larger premises became even more urgent. Jeanette now found an unfurnished three-roomed flat in Follett Street where she shared one room with Joyce. At weekends, the usual influx of children crowded into the tiny hall, sitting-room, bedroom and kitchen. By now Cathy was beginning to respond to Jeanette's quiet, non-violent, uncritical and sympathetic approaches. Although she still manifested bouts of very disturbed behaviour, for the first time in her life, the girl knew what it was like to feel that somebody actually cared what became of her. Her greatest fear was that she might be sent home.

'I don't never want to go back there!' she said one night. 'I don't want to go to that place Andy's at neither. I want to stay with you! If you let me stay here, I promise I won't break nothing ever again.'

With Robbie due back from Bromley as always for the holidays, the sleeping conditions at the flat worsened. Cathy had a camp-bed in the sitting-room and there was no privacy for any of them. They seemed always to be falling over each other, and now Robbie's ten-year-old sister, Joan, was in trouble and needed a refuge.

Jeanette had kept in touch with Mary Jackson whilst her son was in Bromley, keeping her informed of the boy's progress and somehow finding time to sit and talk to her. Mary was lonely. More and more often, she turned to Jeanette as she might have turned to a parent, to solicit her advice when a decision had to be made, or when she was once again in debt. She was not only inept in caring for herself and her family, but incapable of doing so.

Because of her mother's inadequacies, it fell to Joan most of the time to look after her five-year-old sister, Crissie. Although her school attendance suffered, the girl managed somehow to cope. She was concerned about her appearance and took great trouble to look nice. She was a pretty child with long fair hair curling down to her shoulders, which she obviously attempted to keep brushed and clean. Jeanette or Joyce were always happy to relieve Joan from time to time of her little sister so that she could go off to play for an hour or two with her friends.

But on one particular day, Jeanette was out at work when Joan called by, so the girl decided to take Crissie home. There, to her relief, she found one of her older brothers entertaining his girlfriend.

'Will you keep an eye on Crissie for me?' she asked. 'I want to go out and play.'

Not wishing to appear unkind in front of his girlfriend, the boy agreed to keep an eye on his little sister. A short while later, seeing her settle happily on the floor playing with a doll, he decided to make the most of the rare opportunity for privacy and hastened his girlfriend into the bedroom. Soon after they had disappeared, Crissie decided she was hungry. Within her reach was the chip pan and she ignited the gas. Several minutes passed before the child – looking to see if the fat was hot enough to cook some chips – tipped the scalding liquid over herself, causing horrifying burns.

When Mary finally returned from the hospital where Crissie had been taken, it was not her son, but her daughter, Joan, whom she blamed for the terrible accident, insisting that Crissie had been left in *her* care. The child decided to run away. She went to the only person she knew who might be sympathetic – the school nurse.

Jeanette was home when the telephone rang.

'I've been trying for hours to get hold of the Social Services,' the nurse said. She outlined what she knew of the situation. 'There's no question of Joan agreeing to go home – she's scared stiff and insists her Mum hates her. Could you cope with her, Jeanette? She's quite hysterical. I can't keep her here after school closes.'

Jeanette settled the sobbing child in a bed in her flat, then went round to see Mary in the vain hope of effecting some kind of reconciliation.

'I don't want her back!' Mary shouted. 'I don't care what you do with her – I don't want to see her ever again. It's all her fault – she can't be trusted to do nothing – and now Crissie's in hospital and, like as not, I'll be blamed. No, I'm not having her home and that's final.'

Jeanette contacted the Social Services next morning. It

seemed that Joan had been on their 'At Risk' register for a long time and now the social worker was grateful for the opportunity to have the girl put in Care.

'Will you foster her for the time being, Jeanette?' the social worker asked. 'She knows you, and after the shock she's had, poor kid, a strange environment – even if we *could* rustle up some foster parents who, I might say, are pretty thin on the ground right now – would be bound to add to her confusion.'

It did not occur to either woman that Jeanette had not officially been designated a suitable foster mother, nor had her home vetted, although Robbie and Cathy were already officially in her care. Now, once again, the regulations were ignored.

'We'll pay the usual allowance for Joan,' the social worker said. 'Let me know if you have problems, Jeanette. I'll be round to see her in a day or two.'

Later that evening when Joyce returned from work, she listened to Jeanette's explanations for the new arrival. Since Jeanette never invited her opinion, she kept her misgivings to herself. She could understand why Jeanette felt she must take Joan in. The girl had always been the family scapegoat and Mrs Jackson took no trouble to hide the fact that she actively disliked her daughter. Where she would spend money quite generously on presents for Robbie, Joan received gifts that were either unwanted items her mother wished to be rid of, or something that had been used or damaged . . . a jumper with the ribbing unravelled, a half-empty bottle of scent. The cruelty was deliberate and did not go unnoticed by the child who, being a regular attender at the Club, would often reveal her distress.

But Joyce now felt that Jeanette was already stretched to the limit. She looked worn out. Admittedly it would be less of a strain on her once Robbie returned from Bromley at the end of term to live permanently at the flat. She would not have that constant driving to and from Bromley to cope with as well as the Club meetings, the weekend kids and Cathy's violent tantrums. It would save a bit of money also, she realised, with less petrol to buy. Nor would she have to go on paying her mother for Robbie's keep. Mary Jackson had at last agreed to Jeanette's fostering of Robbie, which meant she would have the same allowances for him as would be paid for Joan.

The slight easing of their financial budget was one worry less. The thought reinforced Joyce's belief that neither of them should bother about the long-term future since the pattern of their lives was already ordained.

'Get yourself off to bed, Jeanette! You look exhausted,' she said practically. 'I'll sit up with Joan until she falls asleep.'

The fact that she had taken on the responsibility for yet another child did not weigh heavily on Jeanette's mind. If anything, she was even more convinced that this was the kind of work she was meant to be doing. Once, she had been so sure that she was destined for nursing – a job she still enjoyed doing. At the root of her growing commitment to these disturbed and abused children was the change in her attitude to life. She was now a Christian and had also reached the conclusion held by Joyce: that God controlled her destiny. By bringing the children to her door, He was showing her the way He wanted her to go. It was God's will, she decided, which was motivating her.

To Joyce, she remained an enigma, never talking about herself or her past or encouraging confidences. They were friends and working colleagues, but the friendship was always at arm's length. It sometimes surprised Joyce that Jeanette showed so little sign of appreciating her own worth. She once remarked to her, 'Whatever these kids do – bedwetting, soiling themselves, swearing, fighting, screaming their heads off – you take it in your stride. And sooner or later they all pay attention to what you say to them in that determined voice of yours!'

'Someone's got to keep calm,' was Jeanette's comment. 'I don't see any reason why they shouldn't respond at least to minimum discipline without violence. Of course, they've lived so long on the brink of violence, their breaking point is pretty near the surface. That's why I don't blow a fuse when they break the rules – not if I know they're doing their best!'

In Jeanette's opinion, these children could not be treated like ordinary kids. They had to learn what love was. This was basically what she tried to teach them – that no matter how awful other people thought them or how bad they thought

52

themselves, they were human beings and they mattered – if to no one else, then to God and to her.

In her attempts to convince them of this, she would begin by asking them what they considered to be the most valuable thing they could think of. Their replies varied from jewellery to a car, a palace, an aeroplane... depending on their ages and interests. Patiently, she would point out to them that human life was the most valuable thing in the world; that they were human beings and therefore more valuable than any car, aeroplane or palace.

Jeanette believed very strongly that the children had rights and impressed upon them her intention always to be their advocate because she cared about them; that she would fight for their rights, no matter who she offended in the process, or what the repercussions for herself might be. She had already fought for Robbie's right to a normal State education and in future years, when the occasion demanded, she would do battle with equal fervour and persistence for her other children whose needs conflicted with bureaucratic decisions.

Gradually, Jeanette's philosophy was having its effect upon Cathy. She went for a whole week without breaking anything; she stopped hitting her or Joyce, and now took her anger out on the other kids. It was progress of a sort. Jeanette deliberately put a certain amount of trust in the girl. When the other children departed after their brief weekend respite, she always asked Cathy to escort little Tom home. This Cathy did to please Jeanette, although she was scared stiff of her family and hated going there.

Cathy's fear of the violence within her home was not without foundation. Tom arrived the following weekend with the whole of his back, from his shoulder blades down to his thighs, black and purple with livid contusions. He was very quiet but, when questioned by Jeanette, explained that his Mum had hit him with a broom.

Naturally enough, he was very reluctant to return home that Sunday night, but Jeanette knew he had to go to school next day and, having made him change into his clean clothes, she told Cathy to take him back to his family. Within the hour, they returned. Cathy handed Jeanette a note from their mother.

'I can't look after him no more. Cathy says you'll have him so I'm sending him back...'

Jeanette made room for the boy, providing him with a camp-bed in the hall whilst avoiding Joyce's questioning gaze.

'It's just for tonight, Joyce,' she defended herself, well aware that the flat was already hopelessly overcrowded. 'I'm not keeping him longer. If his Mum can't keep him, it's up to his social worker to find him a decent foster home. I'm well aware I *can't* take on any more kids on a permanent basis, so wipe that scowl off your face!'

The social worker came to see her next day. She looked harassed.

'I've talked to Tom's mother – but I don't have to tell you what she's like! She swears she hasn't hit the boy – says his brother's responsible; so we can't take her to court. But one thing's certain, Jeanette, Tom can't go back home. He's not safe there.' She had been deeply shocked by the sight of Tom's back and her expression was apologetic as she added: 'We've suspected for a long time that he was at risk so I suppose we should have removed him before this happened. I'm really sorry about it.'

She stared uneasily round the cluttered room. Whatever else was said in support of Jeanette as a foster parent, this place could not possibly be considered an adequate home by the authorities. Moreover, the regulations usually required two parents to foster – and Jeanette was unmarried. Yet where else could she – the boy's social worker – find a place for him at such short notice? When she'd spoken to the boy earlier, he had begged her to let him stay here...

'It would only be for two to three months, Jeanette, whilst I investigate the problems at home,' she said tentatively. 'And you do have his sister here to help keep an eye on him...'

Jeanette's mouth tightened.

'I suppose it's easy to say with hindsight that he ought to have been removed from home long ago. He was one of the first kids to come to the Club and we all knew then he wasn't being properly looked after...'

She was interrupted by the sound of the door opening. Cathy

54

stood there glaring at the social worker, her arm protectively round her little brother's shoulders.

'If you've come to take 'im 'ome, you can fuckin' fink again!' she declared violently. ''e ain't leaving Jeanette's and that's it straight!'

Tom's small, angry voice supported her.

'I ain't goin' nowhere,' he said, 'and no one...' he glared defiantly at his social worker, '... *no one* can't make me. I'm stayin' 'ere wiv Jeanette.'

Chapter 6

'Three children die every week following abuse or neglect at the hands of their parents' (NSPCC estimate, 1985)*

There were now four permanent members of Jeanette's family. She was officially Robbie's foster mother; Tom and Robbie's sister, Joan, were still with her; and Tom's sister, Cathy, had not after all been despatched to a psychiatric unit. She had quietened down considerably and Jeanette had persuaded the headmistress who had expelled the girl to give her another chance and reinstate her.

That winter, Jeanette, Joyce and the children moved to a slightly larger two-bedroomed house in Hartfield Terrace; but with six in the family of mixed ages and sexes, they were still hopelessly overcrowded and it was necessary to partition the bedrooms and make a third bedroom of the sitting-room. When Jeanette had time to sit, it was of necessity in the kitchen.

She was still working, at present as an Industrial Nurse, attending to the needs of the workers at three different factories. Whilst during the term time, she could just manage to continue the supervision of the children and cater for their physical well-being, this became an impossibility once the holidays started or if one of the children were ill. In fine weather, she could leave them in a nearby park where she could, from time to time, make sure they were not up to mischief. But this arrangement was totally unsuitable in bad weather and Jeanette realised that she

---

*Other statisticians estimate double this number.

56

must give up her job no matter how seriously this would undermine her precarious financial situation. Determined somehow to make ends meet, she gave in her notice.

She was now receiving the foster care allowance for all four children, but the inadequacy of the allowance barely covered their basic needs and took no account of any damage they might do. Breakages were a normal daily occurence since all the children were subject to outbursts of uncontrolled rage. Jeanette understood that these were not destructive tantrums but the only way her emotionally damaged, unwanted kids could find relief when they felt unable to cope with a situation. At such moments, she put her arms round them and rocked them until they had regained a degree of self-control.

Jeanette and Joyce pooled their salaries and from time to time, Baptist friends from their church raised small sums or made donations of clothes or household articles which Jeanette needed. Her own background of privation helped her to manage somehow. The children were used to going without toys and accepted the conditions as normal. The two big luxuries for them in this new phase of their lives were that they were fed regularly and there was a total absence of violence. No matter how badly they behaved, Jeanette never raised her hand to them. Indeed, she seldom raised her voice. She knew only too well the uselessness of violence. The children had long ago learned to shut themselves off from pain, just as she herself had once learned to escape from reality. They did not cry if they were hurt – what use were tears? What they needed to learn was that life could be very different from the type of existence they took for granted; that not everyone hated each other and the world they lived in; that there were people who cared for each other and that there was such a thing as love.

Jeanette never pretended to the children when they first came to live with her that she loved them, but made a point of stressing that she cared very deeply about them and that from caring, love could grow; that meanwhile, she accepted them as they were. She believed that any pretence of love would be quickly sensed by a child and could only be harmful to any future relationship. She recognised these children's desperate need for a chance to grow up as human beings; for a chance to make normal relationships with people; for the right to respect themselves as well as others.

Deeply aware of the abyss of loneliness and despair she and they had once lived in, it was not always easy for her to accept that a benign God should permit so much unhappiness in the world.

She was deeply concerned about the effects of the broken marriage of a couple whose children she had occasionally looked after in order to give the parents a chance to resolve their personal problems. Her efforts had proved useless and now the wife, Bridget, who had custody of the five children, was cohabiting with a man who regularly beat up the children. One of them, a ten-year-old boy called Martin, who had not yet learned the wisdom of keeping clear of confrontation, was the particular butt of the man's violence. Concerned for the child, Jeanette called one Friday night to see him. Bridget was screaming as she opened the door and dragged her inside.

'Quickly, quickly!' she shouted. 'Len is killing Martin. Thank God you've come...'

The boy was lying on the floor, straddled by Len, who was ramming his fist into the child's face again and again. Horrified, Jeanette took hold of Len and, regardless of his size, managed to haul him backwards, shouting at Martin to run away as she did so. Despite the blows Len rained on her, she, too, managed to get out of the house. Martin was already in the car, so terrified that he had locked all the doors. Len grabbed hold of Jeanette, and Martin, realising the danger she was in, opened the driver's door. He slammed it quickly, catching her foot agonizingly in his haste, but not before Len had landed a further number of vicious blows on Jeanette's head.

Somehow, despite the pain in her foot and the blood streaming down her face, Jeanette managed to drive away from the house before, on the point of collapse, she was obliged to pull up. A passer-by called the police and took Martin and herself to the police station. Len had already been in prison for assault – he'd once broken Bridget's jaw – and the police were anxious that Jeanette should press charges.

She agreed to do so, but it was a decision she was to regret. She had no option but to return the child to his home after the

weekend, after which Len telephoned, threating that if she did
not drop the charges the children would be made to suffer. The
following week one of Martin's brothers had a broken arm and
although Jeanette was told when she called to collect the boys
for the weekend that he had fallen off a wall, she knew that Len
had carried out his threat. She dropped the charges.

The Social Services felt that in all the circumstances, it would
be better if Jeanette stayed away from the family, leaving them
to make regular checks on the children. They visited every week,
and from then on, Jeanette telephoned one of the social workers
every Friday night to reassure herself that the children were all
right. Jeanette had quite enough responsibilities of her own and
although she worried about Bridget's boys, she was relieved to
know that she need no longer be actively involved with the
family.

They were in her thoughts as she stood one morning at the
tiny sink in the kitchen washing up the dishes from their Sunday
breakfast.

Robbie, now ten years old, put his head round the door.

'It's Arthur Gow from the London Mission,' he said. 'He's
got some kids with him . . . the Cook kids what live next door to
him.'

Jeanette put down the dishcloth and wiped her hands on her
apron.

'Take Tom and the others into the bedroom,' she told him,
sensing that if Arthur Gow were here with five children,
something must be very wrong.

The children, who stood huddled together in the corner of the
small sitting-room, were white-faced, unkempt, the four girls
closely resembling one another with dark hair and dark brown
eyes. Only the little boy was fair-haired and blue-eyed. Jeanette
knew all five of them – and their parents.

Mrs Cook was an alcoholic, a drug addict and a prostitute
and had driven her partially deaf husband to such a state of
despair that Jeanette had once discovered him writing a suicide
note. His despair had finally manifested itself in violence and
not only did he break everything he could damage in the house in
his fits of rage, but he frequently attacked his wife. The children
were witnesses. They had once found their mother lying on the

floor bleeding uncontrollably and had supposed her to be dead.

The twins, Gary and Ellen, were the youngest and a short while ago, Jeanette had given a little party for them for their third birthday. The three girls, aged five, seven and nine, had all been 'In Care' on a number of different occasions because of their mother's neglect.

The brief moment of silence as Jeanette came into the room was short-lived. The girls started shouting, screaming, crying hysterically. Quietening them temporarily with the offer of food, she managed to elicit from the harrassed Mission worker what had happened. The mother had not returned home the previous night. A neighbour had heard the children screaming and found that the father, too, was absent. The interior of the house was totally wrecked and not knowing what else to do, the neighbour had called in Arthur Gow, who had brought them to Jeanette.

'I couldn't think what else to do with them,' he said apologetically. 'Being the weekend, there's no one in the Social Services offices. Can you cope, Jeanette?'

'I can't keep them here – I haven't the room!' Jeanette said firmly, but after a quick glance at the white faces of the twins, she relented. 'If there's really nowhere else for them to go, they can stay till Monday. I'll contact Social Services then and they'll have to find a place for them.'

By Monday morning, Jeanette's resolve not to be burdened with any more responsibility had hardened into total resolution. The children were like animals, the twins grabbing at any food in sight and cramming it into their mouths. They even stuffed themselves with the cat food put out for Joyce's pet on the kitchen floor. When they were not searching for food, they climbed on the furniture, tore down the curtains, ripped their own and everyone else's clothes, urinated and soiled wherever and whenever the need took them. The three girls, whilst less destructive, remained hysterical and beyond any attempts to reassure or reason with them.

The decisions reached that Monday morning during Jeanette's visit to the Social Services offices left her with mixed feelings of resignation and guilt. It had been agreed that there was no alternative for the three girls but to send them to a

Children's Home in Essex. Jeanette knew what this meant: there would be several houses with house parents and staff who were constantly changing. They did their best for the children, but by the very nature of their jobs, there was no personal care, no continuity for children in desperate need of someone they could trust, cling to, depend upon. Their physical, but not their emotional needs would be met. She knew, too, that so often in Children's Homes, the innocents – if such they could be called – were soon taught how to lie, steal, bully, damage. Very often, there were cases of sexual abuse by older children of the younger. Even members of staff, had on occasions been found culpable.

Jeanette herself went with the social worker and the girls to the Home, trying as best she could to reassure them. All three fought violently and attempted to escape through an open window. They had finally to be locked in their bedroom.

Jeanette left with a very heavy heart, believing she had denied them any hope of a normal family life.

She had agreed to keep the twins, Gary and Ellen, for a month until suitable foster parents were found for them since there was little else to be done with them. The local Children's Home where they had already spent some time had refused categorically to take them in again on account of their parents' disruptiveness.

Jeanette and Joyce were very quickly to understand why the Home had rejected the twins. They were so uncontrollable that Joan could be heard during their customary evening prayers praying that a foster home would very soon be forthcoming!

But it was not. The month passed – and another month. The twins were left by the Social Services in Jeanette's care. By this time, a visiting social worker had discovered that Jeanette had never been vetted by the authorities for official approval as a foster parent. It was, however, to be a further year before she was finally vetted, as a formality, and then approved – by which time she had six foster children officially in her care.

In the meantime, Jeanette's hands were full with the Cook twins. Neither child spoke of their home or parents, but the effects of the violence they had encountered manifested themselves in many different ways. Gary clung to his sister, never even partially at ease if she were out of sight. At night, he would pick endlessly at his blankets, nibbling great gaping holes in them. Both Joyce and Jeanette went constantly into see him, afraid that he would choke on the woollen pieces he stuffed into his mouth. In the daytime, he would even chew holes in his jumper. He had frequent nightmares and often sleepwalked.

Ellen, in her turn, clung to Jeanette. Both children backed away if any attempt were made to touch them yet the little girl seemed to derive a sense of security by attaching herself to some part of Jeanette's clothing. She would grab hold of Jeanette's skirt and refuse to let go. At night, Jeanette was obliged to remove her skirt and leave it with the child to cuddle in bed. During the day, she could not even detach the child's grasp when she went to the bathroom and would have to leave a fold of her skirt outside the closed door for Ellen to cling to. It was a lifeline Ellen would not relinquish for several years to come. She would not talk, although Jeanette did what she could to encourage her to communicate by talking to her; but although occasionally as time went by the little girl would smile and nod, she would not reply. But there was progress of a sort. Jeanette finally persuaded Ellen to allow her to hold her hand. Whenever possible, Jeanette did her work around the house one-handed so that she could retain this tenuous physical contact with the child.

Gary's progress was much slower. He was frequently hysterical, throwing himself around the room like a caged animal. Of the two children he seemed less able to cope with his past memories, although neither child was able to cope with the newest developments. The Social Services had obtained a Court Order for their removal from the parents and for them to be fostered by Jeanette; but the Order allowed parental visiting and Mrs Cook, who had returned to her home, demanded to see them whenever the whim took her.

Jeanette was sympathetic to the parents' desire to see the twins but their visits were disastrous. Their mother was as often as not drunk, and their violent domestic squabbling terrified both Gary and Ellen. It was clear to Jeanette that neither child wished to go out with their parents for the day and, when they did so, they would return in a state of hysteria. The nightmares, the bed-wetting, the sleepwalking would be as bad as it had been when Jeanette had first taken them in five months previously.

The children's visits to their parental home were even more unsettling than the outings. Inevitably the surroundings brought back memories of the violent scenes that had taken place there in the past. More often than not during their visits home, further rows took place. Gary screamed hysterically to go back to Jeanette's house, which so angered his mother that she threatened that Jeanette might lock him up in a cupboard if he went back with her. Ellen suffered too, becoming rigid for days afterwards the moment any attempt was made to discipline her or to touch her. It was understandable to Jeanette, who had experienced the same aversion to any physical contact, but would have proved very distressing to an innocent foster parent eager to give affection and finding it so obviously repulsed.

Jeanette, the twins' social worker and the health visitor, agreed that the parents' contact with them was proving disastrous. A case conference was held at which it was decided to have the children assessed by an educational psychologist and a child psychiatrist. Meanwhile, visiting was restricted to Jeanette's house and only at fortnightly intervals.

The fortnightly visiting at Hartfield Terrace brought a degree of stability into the twins' lives. Very gradually, they began to realise that – as Jeanette kept telling them – their mother could not take them away. They endured the twenty to thirty minutes Mrs Cook spent with them, always anxious to see her preparing to leave. After her departure, their behaviour invariably deteriorated as they allowed themselves to relax.

As with Robbie's mother, Mary, Jeanette now did what she could to befriend the unhappy woman. Whatever her private feelings as to the way the twins' mother had behaved towards her five children, Jeanette knew instinctively that it would be wrong to condemn her, or indeed to criticise her. On the contrary, she went out of her way to find something to praise. Mrs Cook was a victim of her present circumstances. Because of her immaturity, her inadequacies as a person, she was without the resources that might have given her the strength to fight them. Alcohol and drugs were now as much a means of escape for her from an unbearable existence as Bingo had been for Robbie's mother, Mary. She was terrified of her violent husband, but was powerless to prevent that violence, much of which she evoked herself by her own inefficiencies. Now, not unnaturally, her husband blamed her for the removal of the children, and for the stigma thus cast upon him and his home in the eyes of his neighbours.

Meanwhile, Jeanette was taking the twins regularly to the hospital to see the child psychiatrist. As a nurse, she respected the qualifications held by any senior member of staff, but now, as she watched the specialist's attempts to interpret the twins' behaviour and the right treatment for it through their drawings – all of which indicated violence in some form or another – she knew that there would be no real progress until the parental visits were stopped altogether.

The twins started school in September, at first quite willing to attend. But they became more and more reluctant to do so since their mother frequently waited at the school gates in a drunken state creating a disturbance. With the headmistress's cooperation, Jeanette arranged that Gary and Ellen should come out of school half an hour early so that she could collect them before Mrs Cook arrived. The strategy was effective.

As the year wore on, Jeanette did what little the shortage of time and money permitted to stabilise the children's day-to-day lives. At weekends, weather permitting, she and Joyce took the children to the park. With the foster care allowance standing at that time at about five pounds a fortnight for each child, there could be no paid entertainment such as visits to the zoo. But at least the park provided space and freedom for them to run about and play.

They were, however, strangely lonely outings for Joyce despite the presence of the children and Jeanette, who was usually deep in thought. If Joyce attempted to make conversation, as sometimes she did in the evenings in quieter moments at the house, Jeanette's replies were monosyllabic. She never shared her thoughts, fears, opinions, hopes, and seemed as shut inside herself as she had been in the days after they had first met eight years ago.

Sometimes, this apparent lack of any desire on Jeanette's part for a closer friendship hurt and angered Joyce. She was puzzled by Jeanette's seeming unwillingness to share her worries. Yet at the same time her respect for her had steadily deepened as she observed Jeanette's methods of dealing with the children when they were behaving badly. These methods were extremely effective, despite Jeanette's lack of any training in child psychology.

Jeanette, she realised, acted from instinct and ninety-nine times out of a hundred that instinct proved to be right. Robbie had settled down and was doing well at his new school. Now eleven years old, he had joined the boy scouts. Tom was much calmer and attending school regularly. Cathy, though still frequently liable to fits of rage, hysteria and disturbed behaviour, seemed content to be part of the family. Joan, too, had calmed down and was attending school where she was doing sufficiently well not to be expelled again. Both girls helped with the younger children and with the domestic chores.

But the twins' lives were never peaceful for long. Returning one afternoon from the park, Joyce pushed open the front door – it was never locked because Jeanette's principle was that no child should ever find itself locked out from their home, as were so many of the kids who came to her Clubs.

Through the doorway leading into the sitting-room, she and Jeanette saw the blond head of Mrs Cook who, drunk as she so often was, had staggered into the house and passed out on the settee.

Not long afterwards, the household was disrupted again – this time in the middle of the night – by a furious banging on the front door. A distraught taxi-driver demanded if Jeanette knew the occupant of his cab. The woman had apparently given Jeanette's address and whilst he was driving her there, she had calmly removed all her clothes and flung them out of the window. It was Mrs Cook again – too drunk to know what she was doing. Upstairs in their bedroom, the twins had been woken by the sound of their mother's voice and started screaming. Jeanette knew that they were caught once more in the grip of the old terrifying fears. On her next visit to the psychiatrist, she again described the detrimental effect such scenes were having on the twins.

'The security they need is always undermined,' she explained. 'I begin to make progress but until they can cease feeling afraid, they won't maintain it – not until they feel safe – and that means an end to parental visiting!' she added emphatically. 'You've got to get the visiting stopped. I'm only their foster mother so I can't – but *you* could. If it's only for six months, it would give me a chance to prove I'm right. You've said we're making no lasting progress now – so what's to be lost? Six months – that's all I'm asking for.'

Impressed by Jeanette's obvious sincerity, the psychiatrist agreed to see the twins immediately after one of Mrs Cook's visits. As a consequence, he recommended that the visits should be severely restricted and of a very limited duration. Slowly, as time passed, they began to relax and the many symptoms of their emotional disturbance lessened.

'It's working!' Jeanette thought happily some months later, and because it was the twins' birthday, she stopped at a toy shop and bought them a doll's house, complete with doors, windows and furniture. The children were entranced and settled down to play, their delight showing in rare smiles of pleasure.

But an hour later, Ellen came running to her in tears. Jeanette went into the room where they had been playing and was horrified to find that most of the furniture, the little staircase and all the windows had been smashed in.

Wordlessly, Ellen pointed at Gary who had clearly done the damage, although his expression showed no signs of guilt.

Jeanette knelt down beside him, longing to touch him yet knowing he would not allow it.

'Why, Gary, *why?*' she asked, striving to keep her voice calm.

For once he returned her gaze. They had been playing mothers and fathers, he explained. His blue eyes were innocent and guileless as he stared back at her, adding matter-of-factly, 'and I'm the Dad!'

Chapter 7

'40% of the 44,100 children comprising the
NSPCC's casework in an average year are
under five years old...'
(NSPCC casework statistics, 1986)

Jeanette now had six disturbed children in her care. She and
Joyce had moved once again – this time to a three-bedroomed
council house in Old Ford Road. Although more spacious, the
condition of the house was appalling and quite literally falling
around them.

Jeanette managed to maintain both order and cleanliness in
the chaos that often ensued when the council workmen were
attempting to replace floorboards, plaster walls or put in new
electric cables. There was a degree of obsessiveness in her
determination to have law and order within her household since
there had been a desperate lack of either throughout her
childhood. Moreover, tidiness was an absolute essential in the
overcrowded conditions in which she, Joyce and the children
lived. It remained a firm rule that every child had their own bed,
their own space, their own container in which to keep their own
possessions – a privilege previously unknown to them. It gave
them an added sense of orderliness in their lives.

Similar unhappy childhood memories prompted Jeanette to
maintain a strict family budget. Nothing was ever bought that
could not be paid for. On one occasion when, despite the
pooling of hers and Joyce's salaries, the lack of money was so
acute that they were unsure where the next pound note was

coming from, Jeanette suggested a prayer as a last alternative. As she opened her Bible, a £5 note which she had put by for a rainy day, fluttered from between the pages onto the floor.

'Cor!' remarked one of the children at this tangible proof of a miracle. 'That was quick!'

Jeanette was always short of time too. There was the housework, the cooking, the shopping, the washing and ironing, the children to be got to school, to be nursed when they went down with the usual childhood diseases. There were visits from their various social workers and health visitors whose jobs were to check on the foster children in her care. There were the visits from or to the children's natural parents which nearly always resulted in time-consuming emotional reaction afterwards.

There was even a totally unexpected visit from a four-year-old girl called Geraldine. Uninvited, the diminutive West Indian child followed Tom into the house one afternoon when he returned from school and hungrily devoured the tea Jeanette had put ready for him.

Later Jeanette discovered a note in the little suitcase the child had brought with her.

'I've come down from the north looking for work and somewhere to live. I've heard you're a Christian family. Would you look after Geraldine for me until I collect her?'

It was late on a Friday afternoon and the social worker Jeanette telephoned to report that a child had landed on her doorstep, was unable to make proper arrangements for her. Geraldine remained for a week, at which point she was handed over to her grandmother whose whereabouts had finally been discovered. Geraldine had settled down so contentedly she was unwilling to leave!

Sometimes Jeanette was so tired she would fall into bed, praying that just for once she would not have a broken night with one or other of the children screaming in a nightmare or, in Gary's case, sleepwalking. Such nights were very rare and next morning there were always the wet nightclothes and bedding to be dealt with.

On one such night, Jeanette was herself responsible for one of

Gary's many setbacks. Her sister, Betsy, dropped in to see Jeanette with George, her husband. Believing that the twins might like to see this 'uncle', she had taken George to their room to say goodnight to them.

Gary began screaming in abject terror. Too late, Jeanette realised that she should have foreseen the child might associate an adult male with his father and suffer all the fears his memory evoked. In future, she would ensure that the little boy's encounters with men took place in broad daylight where he could safely distinguish their features.

Jeanette's relationship with her younger sister had remained one of deep affection, but it was marred by the past. Betsy had adopted their mother's attitude to the events of their childhood. It was something to be forgotten, to be buried as deep as possible and never to be discussed. When Betsy had first married George, she had set about trying to find Jeanette a husband, wanting her to have a normal marriage and family life because this would prove that no lasting damage had been done by her father. When Jeanette tried to explain that any intimate relationship with a man would always be impossible for her precisely because of what had happened, Betsy had replied: 'But you've got to forget all that – it's not important now.'

Sensitive to Betsy's distress, Jeanette did not pursue the subject, although part of her longed to be able to discuss it openly – if not with her sister, then with her mother. Their anxiety to sweep the truth into a dark corner left her isolated and with the illogical fear that perhaps after all, she had in some way been at fault. As a nurse, she knew perfectly well that incest was not a hereditary disease, but she now wondered if Betsy feared that their father's evil 'traits' might be passed down to the next generation. Even Jeanette's brother, Alan, who was considered to have an exceptionally good brain and was now a highly qualified electrical engineer, seemed to prefer to pretend that nothing untoward had happened and that Jeanette had no cause to feel herself a victim.

Jeanette had given over the care of her Bible Clubs to friends. She was now convinced that the Baptist way of life was the one she must follow. She did not worry any more about the next day, week, month, year, believing firmly that God had destined her for this particular path and not, as she had once supposed, for nursing. In retrospect, she could see why she herself had had to suffer in her own childhood since now it helped her to understand and assist these other young lives for whom she had made herself responsible. She realised that the concept of a mystical Heavenly Father was difficult for the children to grasp, especially the younger ones. Many had fathers or stepfathers who physically abused them and, as Gary had reacted to the sight of a male figure appearing by his bed, they, too, were fearful of any father figure. Patiently, Jeanette tried both at home and at her Bible Club meetings to explain that the Heavenly Father, God the Father, was a benign, loving and caring person who was perfect; that in the same way as they could not visibly see why light appeared when they pressed a switch, they could not see Him, but that He *was* there, both in this world and in Heaven.

In this way she tried to help them to understand so that they could draw comfort, as she did, from the thought of Someone who cared about them and that their lives could change if they adopted His teaching and followed His concepts of right and wrong.

It was inherent in all of the children to lie and to steal. Even now, after six years, Robbie had not fully appreciated the ethics she tried continually to teach all the children during their evening family prayers. He came home from school one day, delight and pride written all over his face as he beamed at her, shoving a parcel into her hands.

' 'S a present for you, Mum,' he said. Since he had officially become her foster child, he had started to call her 'Mum' and now, quite often, the younger children did likewise.

Jeanette gazed at the china ornament with dismay. She could guess its value and knew that Robbie did not have such a sum to spend.

'Where did you get it?' she asked in her quiet voice.

'Nicked it from Woolies!' he said at once. 'Don't you like it?'

'I like it very much and I appreciate the thought, Robbie, but I've told you again and again, it's wrong to steal things from other people. You know that.'

'But it ain't fer me I got it. 'S fer you...'

Jeanette reached for her coat.

'Stealing is stealing, whoever you steal from or for. It's got to go back, Robbie. I'll come with you. If you say you are sorry and regret what you did, maybe they'll overlook it this once...'

She hated destroying Robbie's pleasure in giving, yet knew it must be done. Robbie was reprimanded by the manager, but the matter was not reported to the police. Although he sulked for several days afterwards, he made no attempt at retribution and continued to work hard and do well at school.

It was obvious to Jeanette that she was not making the same steady headway with Cathy. The pattern of her behaviour had been too well established by the time she had come to live with Jeanette for her new way of life to have a great deal of effect. She was adolescent and quite unable to deal with her emotions. Her frequent outbursts of rage and destructiveness affected the other children and when her social worker suggested she should attend a nearby psychiatric unit, Jeanette agreed it might help.

At first, Cathy was reluctant to keep the appointments, but once she had established that nothing more dreadful happened to her at the unit than to be asked to talk about herself, she went without fuss. Now aged seventeen, she began to demand her independence. Jeanette found her a job as a domestic help in a private house where she settled down quite happily. Bearing in mind how little money she had ever had before, she might well have spent her weekly wage upon herself. Yet every pay day, of her own accord, she gave each child some pocket money.

Cathy was anxious to have a flat of her own, a need to which the housing authority was sympathetic, and in June, as soon as she was eighteen, she was allocated a tiny one-roomed flat. At the same time, she ceased to come within the fostering age and, theoretically, Jeanette had no further responsibility for her. Nevertheless, she visited the girl frequently, reassuring herself that Cathy was making progress at the psychiatric unit and was coping satisfactorily with her job.

'I care what happens to you, Cathy, always remember that,' she told her whenever they met at Cathy's flat or when the girl came to visit the Family.

One afternoon, the Head of the local Social Services Fostering and Adoption Section sent a social worker, Rosemary Wolfson, round to see Jeanette about one of their children. 'She's in need of representation but has no social worker,' Rosemary said as she sat at the kitchen table in Jeanette's house sharing a cup of tea with her before the children returned from school. 'Her case only came up by chance when we were attending the review of another kid. I want to talk to you about this little girl, Jeanette. I thought maybe you could help...'

For some time now there had been a serious shortage of social workers. Many of them had no training and for those who had, the training given them was inadequate. Because of the shortage of manpower, the newly qualified workers, often very young, could not get the support and back-up (as was mandatory) of the more senior members of staff. In inner-city areas where poverty and deprivation aggravated the need for children to be put 'In Care', there were proportionately fewer workers per head of population than were employed by more affluent and crime-free areas. Around 50% of the children had no social workers and in general only emergency cases were covered.

No one enjoyed working in such depressing circumstances where they did not feel they were coping with their responsibilities adequately. Many left to go to more pleasant surroundings; or, if they had been too greatly disillusioned, to different jobs altogether.

Jeanette realised the implications for a child without representation and the possible consequences were in her mind as she listened to Rosemary's story.

Ten years previously, Natalie had been born to parents of mixed race. Unwanted at birth, she had been left at the Social Services offices. What seemed the perfect solution was found. A family of mixed race offered a foster home for the baby, who was in age a twin to their fifth child, a boy.

Natalie was taken into the family on a permanent fostering basis. No one, it seemed, had counselled the foster parents, and the little girl was brought up to believe she was the boy's true twin. The arrangement was perfectly happy until she started school where, because of the regulations, she was registered in her real surname. When she had asked her parents why she had a different name, they had no option but to tell her the truth.

The shock had been traumatic; the child was unwilling – and quite unable – to accept the facts. Then, suddenly, it seemed as if the situation had improved. The foster parents told the little girl that they would adopt her so that she would really become part of their family.

'So what went wrong?' Jeanette asked, knowing that this story did not have a happy ending.

Rosemary's face looked momentarily defeated.

'I don't know the ins and the outs of it but there were difficulties with the foster father. Natalie was put in the care of the Children's Department who placed her in a Home – as a temporary measure, her foster parents had said, whilst they arranged her adoption. It would be only for a few weeks...' Rosemary shrugged, her eyes reflecting her emotions.

That was *over a year* ago. Attempts were made to tell Natalie that her foster family would not be adopting her after all, but she refused to accept it. Her foster parents never tried to see her, write to her, contact her. Any attempt to convince her that they had never intended to adopt her when they had sent her to the Children's Home was met by a furious denial... 'They'll come for me soon, you see if they don't!' Her behaviour worsened.

It seemed that Natalie was suspected of having tried to drown one of the younger children by holding its head down in the toilet bowl. Moved by the child's story, Jeanette's heart filled with compassion.

'I'll go and see her,' she said.

But Natalie had not the slightest intention of becoming part of Jeanette's family. When Jeanette arrived at the Home, she was informed by the House Mother that the girl could not be found. Glancing around, Jeanette glimpsed a small face peering down at her from behind the bannisters of the upstairs landing.

'I dare say she'll turn up,' she said in a tone she knew Natalie must hear. 'Perhaps we can go into the sitting-room and I'll wait until she appears.'

Whilst she and the House Mother fabricated a conversation in loud, casual voices, Natalie's curiosity overcame her and she slid unobtrusively into the room and hid behind Jeanette's chair.

'I do hope we see her soon,' Jeanette said, 'as I don't intend to go home until I've met her. I want to tell her that I think she would like living with us and that the children are looking forward to meeting her.'

'What's your house like?'

The child crept into view as Jeanette gave an elaborate description of the home Natalie would be living in.

'I'm not going anywhere,' she whispered. 'You can't make me. I'm staying 'ere.'

Jeanette said gently:

'Why not come and see for yourself? There's six other kids in the family and they'll all be pleased to have you with us. We don't have so many rules and regulations as you do here. I think you'd like it.'

But clearly Natalie felt the devil she knew was better than the devil she didn't know! The choice, however, was not hers. Rosemary was in no doubt that an alternative to the Children's Home was desirable and that the little girl would be properly cared for and counselled at Jeanette's.

Two days later, Jeanette collected her still unwilling guest. By the second day, the quiet, withdrawn child had turned into a small virago.

'I ain't staying 'ere,' she shouted at Jeanette. 'You can't make me!'

Jeanette looked at the pale, distraught face, at the wild tangle of black hair, at the rigid set of the child's mouth. The dark eyes avoided hers. The jaw muscles were clenched.

'You are staying here, Natalie, and the sooner you get used to the idea the better.'

'I ain't staying. I'll run away. I'll go back to the Home . . .' She turned now and looked Jeanette squarely in the face. A look of weariness at the stupidity of adults had replaced the stubborn resistance. 'Doan' you know nothing, you stupid cow?' she said scornfully. 'Doan' you know me Mum and Dad are going to adopt me and I'll be going home to live with me *own* family? How in fucking 'ell are they going to find me if I ain't at the Home when they come?'

Unpalatable though the truth would be for Natalie, Jeanette knew instinctively that the little girl would never be able to cope with her life or her emotions as long as she continued to live in

74

the past. She began her rehabilitation by persuading her that she might as well wait for her parents at Old Ford Road as at the Children's Home. Natalie finally agreed to remain with the Family since, she announced, it would only be for a month or two anyway before her adoption went through and her parents would come for her. She wouldn't be staying long...

In all her dealings with the different children she now fostered, Jeanette's policy remained one of total honesty. They must learn to trust her and this could only come about if they knew that whatever she told them was the truth.

Natalie fought determinedly against it.

'I got a family of me own... I doan' need you. Me Mum and Dad...'

At this point, Jeanette always interrupted.

'No, Natalie, you mean your *foster* Mum and Dad – and they are *not* going to adopt you. You won't be going back to live with them because they don't want you. But we want you – Joyce and me and the kids. We're going to be your new family.'

It was, Jeanette accepted, brutal, but for almost half her life, Natalie had been waiting for the impossible. Because of her desperate need to believe in it, she had convinced herself her foster family still loved her, wanted her. Now she tried to convince Jeanette.

'You doan' believe me, do you. Look, I'll show you pictures. See, that's me Mum – and that's me twin brother and that's me and...'

'No, Natalie, you know that isn't your real family. They were your foster family – that's *all* they were – your *foster* family.'

Jeanette was not unduly worried by the little girl's swearing, stealing, truancy from school. She was far more concerned about her terrible nightmares. Night after night Natalie would wake screaming, insisting that there were hands on her bed, searching for her, creeping towards her. Her terror was very real. Jeanette tried sitting with her, talking to her, but nothing would calm her fear. She tried taking her into her own bedroom, putting Joan with her... but still she woke each night in the grip of ungovernable horrors. Jeanette had no way of knowing what had caused them, although she did wonder at the child's possible ordeal at the hands of her foster father. This would explain why Natalie had not, after all, been adopted. But there was no social services report on the child and she could only surmise the facts.

Before long, Jeanette became exhausted. The sleepless nights were beginning to take their toll since each minute of the day was too fully occupied for the chance of even a brief rest. One night when yet another series of piercing screams dragged her from a deep sleep, her physical fatigue manifested itself in a rare burst of anger. She strode into the child's room and grabbed hold of her wrists.

'Now show me!' she commanded. 'Show me these hands. 'I can't see them. They aren't there. *You* say they are there, so show them to me.'

'There!' Natalie screamed. 'There, there, there!'

'I can't see them! Put my hands on top of them. If they're there, I'll feel them. *Show me!*'

As the child's fingers tentatively felt over the smooth surface of the quilt, her screams turned to soft whimpers.

'They were there – I saw 'em. I did see 'em... they were coming at me...'

'No, you didn't see them because they weren't there – you only dreamed they were there. Feel again, Natalie. They aren't there now, are they? There are no hands...'

For several more nights, Natalie woke screaming, but now of her own accord, when Jeanette put on the light, she would slowly reach out and feel the bedclothes. Her screams became less frantic and finally they and her nightmares stopped.

Jeanette never discovered what dreadful experience the child had endured during her six years with her foster family. She knew only from Natalie herself that those hands reaching out for her *were* those of her foster father... and that they had not been innocently comforting her. Jeanette herself had long since pushed into the back of her mind her own dreadful memories of her father's attentions to her but now, suddenly, her ordeal must have been reawakened deep in her subconscious. As Natalie's nightmares ceased, hers began.

She woke each night, drenched with the sweat of terror as she felt the hands on her bed, reaching out for her, creeping towards her. It was six months before they went as suddenly as they had come. By then, she had far greater worries on her mind to leave room for the imaginary fears of her own and Natalie's dreams.

Chapter 8

'The 1969 Children and Young Persons Act provides fairly precise grounds for taking a child into care. These do not in general terms include the parents' state of mind or capacity as parents. If a child is thriving in spite of a parent's mental illness or alcoholism or drug addiction there may still be very real concern about the safety of the child, but the grounds would not, at least in theory, allow the juvenile court to intervene...'
(William Ackroyd on the Jasmine Beckford Inquiry report, Foster Care magazine, NFCA, 1986)

It was seven years since Jeanette had taken her first child, Robbie, under her wing and she was now fostering six children under the age of fifteen. She had learned in those years how often the system failed to protect abused children. Indeed, the main problem seemed to be that there *was* no co-ordinated system, only a variety of charitable or government sponsored bodies with no overall link with each other and often at loggerheads when decisions of vital importance for the children had to be made.

Astonishingly, the very existence of violence towards babies and children had only been officially recognised in the past decade. Baby battering was not brought to the attention of the public until the 1960s, although it had obviously been a facet of human behaviour for centuries. But in the same way that sex was fast becoming a subject for research and open discussion, so too, was the matter of parental violence, infanticide, incest and various forms of child abuse.

Although there existed long established organisations such as the NSPCC, financed by charity, pressure was now put on governments to allocate funds to deal with these newly acknowledged problems of child welfare. Housing Departments, the Social Services, the Police, schools, hospitals, courts became involved, the various workers responsible to their own departments, as were the various charities to their governing bodies.

The rules for dealing with a case of child abuse varied with the differing organisations: the police, for example, were obliged to treat all serious abuse as a reportable crime; a school teacher was required to report to the Education Department; a hospital doctor to the police. There were, at this time, a bare handful of school psychologists. Since no one existed to put a child's case against classification as uneducable, children like Robbie could all too easily be misjudged and their chance to reach their full potential denied them for life.

The arrest and punishment of a parent who had been guilty of violence towards their child all too often seemed to increase the very family problems which had given rise to violence in the first place. Jeanette had long ago discovered that contrary to public opinion, such parents were not criminals but victims of their own childhood; that their immaturity and complete lack of self-worth made them incapable of behaving differently towards their off-spring – they themselves needed parenting. Yet the policy of the Social Services was rooted in the belief that no foster or adopting parent could replace the blood tie of a natural parent and that the primary aim in the case of any child was to reinstate it with its own parents if this was deemed even remotely possible.

Jeanette had read the report of the inquiry into the death in 1972 of six-year-old Maria Colwell. Despite the serious warnings of the child's school teachers, neighbours, a local shop keeper and devoted foster parents, the Social Service Department had obtained a Court Order for Maria to be returned to her parents – the mother who was known to have had six of her nine children 'In Care' and who had had nineteen changes of address, and a husband with a criminal record including violence.

Jeanette could but hope that the proposed legal changes resulting from the Inquiry would soon be enacted to ensure no such thing could happen again. She knew from her own experience with mothers like Mary Jackson and Mrs Cook that the theory of returning a child to inadequate parents did not – and could not – work out in practise. Perhaps if they had lived alongside neighbours in the way that familes had grouped in streets in pre-war days, the grandmothers, aunts, relatives could have given them the support and relief they needed. All too often, they leaned on their child's social worker and a relationship between the two (encouraged by the social worker) would become such that the interests of the child came very much second.

It was the children, Jeanette felt with deep conviction, who should always be of paramount importance, yet who had no personal representative when the courts ruled on their future. More often than not, the social workers had spent their valuable time trying to help the parents to straighten out their lives and had very limited personal contact with the fostered children. Foster parents, like herself, were not generally included in case conferences or invited to speak for the child in court proceedings, and their valuable first-hand knowledge of a child's problems was never discussed. If given, it was frequently disregarded as being the opinion of an unqualified person.

Jeanette had been invited to attend meetings with a large group of social workers and foster parents like herself, who felt that an association should be formed to allow foster parents a voice in future policy making and to share their experiences and difficulties. As a consequence of those meetings, a charity known as The National Foster Care Association was formed in May 1974. Jeanette was of particular interest to them since the members were aware that despite the overcrowded house and her limited financial resources, she managed her large number of deeply disturbed children as a happy, well-integrated family unit. They were aware too, that she was almost obsessive in her determination to ensure the children's rights and were sometimes made uneasy by her forthright, unequivocal arguments and their effect upon the various authorities with whom the NFCA liaised.

Jeanette's attempts to help her children were hampered at this time by the shortage of social workers – now on strike (a situation compounded by a strike by the Court solicitors). During this period the twins' mother, Mrs Cook, decided that she wanted all her children returned to her from the Children's Home. Since there was no advocate to put the twins' case at the Court hearing, Jeanette was allowed to do so and retained her foster care of them. But she was unable to prevent Ruth, Valerie and Margaret, being returned from the Children's Home to their parents.

Well aware that Mrs Cook was incapable of giving her children proper maternal care, Jeanette was worried about them – and not without cause. Margaret, the youngest, was often to be found playing in the street after midnight and told Jeanette that she was afraid to go home. Matters came to a head when late one night, Jeanette received a telephone call from the local police station. They were holding Margaret, who had asked them to send for her. When Jeanette arrived, she was appalled to learn from the woman police officer who was caring for Margaret that the eight-year-old child was haemorrhaging from the vagina and that she had been violently sexually assaulted. A neighbour had heard Margaret's screams and reported it to the police.

Jeanette never learned who had committed the offence, but since Mrs Cook was in the habit of taking men home, it was assumed one of them was responsible.

The three sisters were immediately returned to the Home, but the emotional damage done to Margaret was irreparable and she had to be placed in a psychiatric unit. Jeanette never saw the girls again, although many years later she heard that Margaret was still receiving psychiatric help. Bitterly, she reflected, the system had failed yet again to put the children's interests first and allowed much unnecessary suffering.

Jeanette's concern for the children in the neighbourhood and her achievements with the six children now in her care was well-known to the hard pressed Social Services departments in her area, and the following January a concerned health visitor asked her if she would consider taking two more children into her family.

Jeanette appreciated that the authorities must be pretty desperate to be inviting her to add two more children to her household. Apart from the overcrowding that had always existed, the state of the house in Old Ford Road was a matter of great concern to everyone: health visitors, social workers, the housing department. The house had been offered to them as a temporary measure only.

Somehow she and Joyce had made the effort to decorate it simply in order to make it habitable. There was only an outside toilet and, although the plumbing worked, the vibration of the washing machine had caused the rotting floor to detach from the wainscotting. Someone had leaned against a mantleshelf in one of the bedrooms, causing the shelf to fall, then the chimney wall and finally the ceiling, which descended on their heads one morning as they were hurrying through breakfast in preparation for school. In all, four floors and five ceilings needed replacing. The wiring was so unsafe, the council had finally sent in an electrician – who took up all the floorboards which had only just been replaced when the walls had been replastered. The family were warned never to use the light switches because they were dangerous and they had to make do with lamps on cables which trailed equally dangerously from room to room.

One of the health visitors was trying desperately to find them a better place to live, but all the council had offered so far were two separate flats. Knowing that she could not possibly manage with the family split into two halves, Jeanette had been obliged to remain in the crumbling old house.

Could she, she wondered, cope with two more children? Had she the time? Although Gary's and Ellen's condition and behaviour had improved, they were still demanding of her time and attention, as indeed was Natalie. The little girl was less hysterical, but still insisted that her stay was only temporary. She was a frequent truant from school.

Cathy, too, was taking up Jeanette's time. She was pregnant, and because of her unwanted condition was once more unable to handle her own emotions, her control over them superficial at

82

best. She was totally convinced that any child born to a member of her family would be mentally or physically handicapped. Nothing Jeanette could say to her convinced her otherwise and with the birth in June only five months distant, she was now threatening to kill the baby when it was born. She was once more receiving psychiatric help at the unit, but Jeanette was deeply disturbed for the future. Although Cathy was no longer her responsiblity, she felt unable to abandon her now she was in trouble.

Tom Robbie and his sister, Joan, were relatively stable and had settled down as permanent members of the household. Robbie had had only one serious set-back as a result of a beating he received for a minor prank from his headmaster. The violence with which the punishment had been administered had brought back to mind the brutal attacks he had suffered in the first six years of his life. He was clearly very frightened and did not wish to go back to school.

Jeanette took him immediately to the Social Services Department to voice her protest; to insist that someone should make the man aware of the harm such treatment could do to violently abused children like Robbie. As a result of her complaint, the headmaster was reprimanded. Her relationship with Robbie was now such that she could talk his ordeal over with him and gradually he came to accept that grown men, even those in authority, were sometimes unable to control themselves.

Jeanette herself was a firm believer in discipline, but her methods of achieving it were unusual. Frequent family conferences were held at which each child old enough was invited to state their point of view. Punishments had first to be mutually agreed by all as being fair. The allocation of responsibilities was equally shared – the older children taking the younger to school, doing the shopping, helping with the washing up, the cooking. Sharing was the rule – not just chores and toys – but all decisions affecting them as a family.

After the health visitor's request that she should take on two more children in need of a family to care for them for a month, Jeanette held a family conference. How would they all feel if she agreed to foster a little boy, Luke, of nine months and his sister,

Sandra, aged just two? There was no hesitation – the children would do what they could to make the newcomers welcome.

The twenty-one-year-old mother of the two new arrivals, Julie, was in a refuge for battered wives. While still in her teens, Julie had had a little girl, and then became pregnant again by the man she lived with. He was a violent man, under the care of a psychiatric social worker, and he had pushed Julie downstairs during a row, insisting the coming baby was not his. From then on, Julie had been convinced that there would be something wrong with the baby, and when her little boy, Luke, was born, she rejected him. Luke had spent the first two months of his life in a foster home. Back with his parents, his father tried to drown him in the bath. Julie took both children and sought refuge in the battered wives' hostel. Recently, Luke had been medically examined at hospital because of his lack of development.

Jeanette was unprepared for the effects of the degree of the little boy's deprivation. His diet had consisted of dried milk given to him in a bottle propped up on a pillow in his cot, and although his weight was normal, he had no muscle tone in his body. He could not even support his own head. If he was put into a sitting position, he immediately flopped over again. Jeanette's children christened him 'Womble'.

The back of his head was bald and flattened because he had lain on his back so continuously. The only movement he made was with his hand upon which his gaze was constantly transfixed. He seemed unaware of any other movement or sound, due, so the health visitor informed Jeanette, to the fact that he had been shut in a room with the curtains drawn for long periods of time and had had no visual or oral stimulation. His thighs and buttocks were covered with sores, and scars from previous sores. Both he and his sister were verminous.

The specialist at the hospital questioned the possibility that Luke might be either brain-damaged or deaf. What was in no doubt was the child's need for adequate love, care and stimulation. His recommendations as to how this could be achieved were passed on to Jeanette, together with advice from the health visitor, social worker, neighbours and friends – all well-intentioned, but combining to leave Jeanette with a feeling of inadequacy, of despair lest she should fail to meet the child's many needs.

She sat on a chair with Luke on her lap and for the first time in a long, long while, she felt dangerously close to tears. How was she to cope? It would take all the twenty-four hours of every day to give him the exercises suggested, take him for walks, stimulate him with play, nurse him. It couldn't be done!

Suddenly, she felt renewed hope. She *could* at least give him an ordinary family life – and with so many children around, he would certainly not lack for stimulation.

'I love you!' she said aloud to the indifferent child on her lap. 'You're going to be part of our family and you're going to grow up to be a strong, happy, sturdy, normal little boy. I'm insisting on it – do you hear me, Luke?'

Jeanette knew her words were incomprehensible to the baby, yet she felt that she had at least made a start – she was communicating with him even if he were not responding to her!

Her first decision was to put Luke in a high-chair by the front gate. Adjoining their house was a shop, a mini-market, and Jeanette reasoned that anyone passing by on their way to it would at least have to see the child and some would talk to him, which indeed proved to be the case. Many of the regular customers came to know him and would enquire after him if he were not in his usual place. There were two old people who often spent as long as an hour 'talking' to the child, thus helping to provide the constant stimulation he needed.

When Luke was not out of doors, she put his high-chair in the passage since no one could walk in or out of the house without seeing him. In any event, he could not be left on a settee or chair lest he fell off or smothered himself on a cushion. She also put Luke's cot on the landing outside the bedroom where, once again, anyone passing him had to notice him and talk to him. When the children were home from school, she laid him on a blanket on the sitting-room floor with his toys around him and the children would take turns playing with him whilst Jeanette got on with the cooking or ironing.

Jeanette had discovered that Luke was terrified of being bathed and now took the child into the bath with her! It was six months before he reached the stage of splashing happily in the water like a normal toddler. By then he was sitting up, taking notice of the other children and watching everything that went on around him. The children were now instructed to take him with them if one of them needed to go to the outside lavatory. The exercise strengthened his leg muscles and within a year he was walking, talking and eating like any child of his age. He was continent in the day, although not yet at night; his sores had healed, but his scars would never disappear.

Sandra like her brother, also showed little sign of having been handled and was very withdrawn. She cried often, sitting herself in a corner during the day and rocking herself continuously. She seemed oblivious to the presence of the other children and spent her time twisting a lock of her hair until it came out, as a result of which she had a bald patch on one side of her head. At night, the two-year-old girl would scream at intervals of fifteen to thirty minutes and Jeanette or Joyce would take it in turns to sit through the night soothing and calming her.

At times like these, Jeanette would silently thank God for bringing her and Joyce together all those years ago, since on so many occasions there was no way she could have coped without Joyce's support. There were many occasions, too, when she realised how invaluable their nursing training was. In her case, she had feared it would be wasted when she had given up her job in order to care for her growing family.

The hospital to whom both children were referred for assessment believed that despite Sandra's current behaviour, she was, in fact, of above average intelligence. It was further proved that Luke was not deaf, as had been suspected, but functioning on the level of a three to four-month-old baby due to the previous lack of stimulation.

All this time Jeanette remained in close contact with his mother, Julie. She did her utmost to reconcile the young woman with both her children. But Julie acted as if her small son did not exist. She got on well enough with little Sandra and sometimes took her out for the day – but never Luke, despite the progress he was making. She was always willing to perform some task for both children if Jeanette asked her, but never initiated help of her own accord.

A case conference was held at which it was decided by the Social Services that Julie might well benefit if she were to spend time with Jeanette at the children's mealtimes and bath times, and learn the basics of good maternal care. Arrangements were

Bob a Job week

School photo

Jeanette with some of her family

The Old Convent

Joyce, 1982

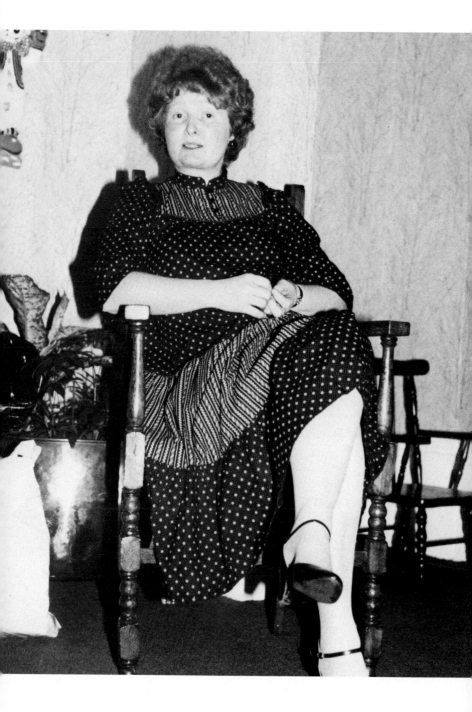

Fun on a motorbike

Story time

A corner of the adventure playground

made for these visits, but when it came to the day Julie would not turn up.

Jeanette submitted her report on the children's progress in readiness for the next case conference on their future, making it clear both that in her opinon returning them to their mother at this stage could be emotionally damaging to them, and that she believed Julie was content to be relieved of the responsibility of looking after them. The departmental decision was to leave Sandra and Luke in Jeanette's care with efforts continuing to involve Julie as often as possible. By now she had been given a flat and had left the battered wives' hostel.

During this time Jeanette had been sent three more children. Catrina and Simon, brother and sister, were aged eleven and thirteen. Catrina arrived first, having run away from her alcoholic mother who, like Julie, had taken refuge with her two children in the battered wives' hostel. Her current boyfriend, a Pakistani, had beaten all three so severely that it had become impossible for them to remain at home. But now Catrina's mother had started beating her daughter and Catrina had run away. She was put in Jeanette's care and a month later, her brother Simon arrived, far from willingly since he had been running wild at the hostel and feared he would lose his independence if he were put back in a family environment.

The third newcomer was an eleven-year-old boy called Mick O'Brien. Jeanette first heard his name when she received a telephone call from one of the local school teachers. The boy had been missing from his own home for several days. He had finally reappeared on a Saturday at the house of the teacher, who had been unable to contact the Social Services to enlist their help. As a last resort, he took Mick round to Jeanette.

She was appalled by her first sight of the boy. He had been sleeping rough since he had run away from the violence at home and was filthy. He was starving and in a state of such high emotional tension that he could not remain still even for a second. His face and hands twitched and his movements were furtive, like those of a wild animal afraid of human contact.

Jeanette agreed to keep the boy over the weekend, to inform the police and Barbara O'Brien that her son was safe, and to get in touch with the Social Services first thing on Monday. When she tried to put her hands reassuringly on Mick's shoulders as she told him he had nothing to fear, he swore at her violently. His reaction to the physical contact caused such extreme rigidity that she knew she must not make the mistake of touching him again.

He ate and drank ravenously, once again like a starving animal, and then prowled the room, his eyes all the while warily watching the other occupants. When finally the teacher rose to go, Mick spoke, not as an eleven-year-old but as a three- or four-year-old.

'Me go! Me no want stay!'

When his teacher told him to sit down, he said violently: 'Fucking won't!'

Later that evening, when the exhausted boy had finally fallen asleep, Jeanette went round to see his mother. At first the woman denied her son had run away, but when eventually the fact that he was with Jeanette had to be admitted, she said she 'didn't fucking care' where he was; she couldn't cope with her large family – it was a story Jeanette had heard so often before.

Barbara O'Brien was not as uncaring as she had tried to make out. The Social Services placed Mick in Jeanette's care for a month, and during that time, his mother was a frequent visitor to Jeanette's home. For some inexplicable reason, she insisted upon doing the ironing or washing up whilst she talked endlessly to Jeanette about her problems. She brought with her little presents for Mick and took him out for rides in a car.

Mick's reaction to finding himself so much the centre of his mother's attention seemed to be one of amazement. He made no attempt to run away, but his behaviour was destructive and disruptive. Unable to communicate with either the adults or the children, he resented their family unity, their shared games, and did what he could to upset them. He appeared immune to their feelings, or indeed, to his own. He suffered the usual nightmares, wet the bed, urinated against the walls of his room and defecated in the cupboards. He stole, grabbed food and pushed it down his throat until he vomited; hid food in cupboards and drawers and under the bed.

Jeanette voiced her misgivings about keeping the boy on a long term basis to the senior social worker and a member of the

Foster Care Department. If she were to cope with the many problems she foresaw, she *must* have their support, she told them. At present, her relationship with Mick's mother was friendly, but Barbara O'Brien might very well turn against her if she thought Jeanette was trying to usurp her place as mother to the boy. If Mick were to go home, she, Jeanette, did not wish to be the one who had to fetch him back. The Social Service Department must be responsible for enforcing the Care Order if it was made.

Jeanette was promised every co-operation. The Care Order was made with visiting rights for Mick's mother. At first, Mrs O'Brien seemed glad that at least the boy was not to be sent to the Children's Home. But Mick himself, realising that he was no longer living with Jeanette on a voluntary basis, began running away whenever Jeanette made the slightest attempt to discipline him. She had only to reprimand him and he would be off. Each time he disappeared, Jeanette made frantic phone calls to his social worker, only to be met by a useless promise that he would discuss the situation with Mick's mother.

Meanwhile, it was Jeanette who had to drop whatever she was doing and go out in search of the boy. Sometimes she would be out all night, asking people in the street if they had seen him, following up every lead and on occasions finding herself having to confront violent and angry men from whose company she must extricate the child.

She was often very frightened and she was frequently anguished because she felt inadequate to prevent Mick's repetitive sorties. She was angry, too, that his social worker was not backing her up. But she would not give up. By now, Mick seemed to expect that she would come searching for him and made her task as difficult as possible, almost as if he were putting her tenacity to the test.

Matters finally came to a head when following an all-night search, Jeanette discovered him in a private flat notorious as a particularly seedy homosexuals' and prostitutes' pick-up point. Dragging the boy outside, she stood him against a wall and stared at him. He had reverted to the state he had been in when she first set eyes on him – face harrowed, muscles twitching, filthy and at bay.

He stared back at her, seeing her exhausted face and eyes

reddened by lack of sleep and emotion. He looked suddenly bewildered.

'Why you keep after me?' he asked. 'Why you keeping coming after me?'

Jeanette kept her voice calm. Her eyes held his gaze although she did not try to touch him.

'I've told you, Mick – because I care about you. Caring isn't just for when you feel like doing it. Caring about someone means all the time, every hour, every day, every week – always.'

There was a momentary flicker of understanding before he shrugged and looked away. But when she moved, he started to follow her. Was it possible, Jeanette asked herself, that at long last she had finally broken through?

Neither spoke again as wearily, side by side, they trudged through the empty dawn-quiet streets towards home.

Chapter 9

'... *the importance of the local authority involving both foster-parents and natural parents at all times in planning and decision-making cannot be over-stressed...*'
(Section 18 of The Child Care Act 1980, quoted by Harry Tunnicliffe, The Law Says..., Pepar Publications, 1985)

There were moments in her life when Jeanette seriously doubted whether she could cope with the heavy responsibilities she had taken upon her shoulders. Living with her that summer were eleven children, each one in need of individual attention and love, and the younger ones were particularly demanding of her time. Joyce, who was now working as a District Nurse Tutor, remained that other vital pair of hands, at the weekends and at night when the traumas of the children's past suffering affected them most keenly.

Her support was invaluable in other ways too. For months now, Cathy had been working herself into a state of hysteria about the coming baby and frequent family conferences were now taking place about its future as well as visits to Cathy's psychiatrist. He was in no doubt that the girl would carry out her threat to 'kill it' the moment the baby was born. But no amount of persuading by Jeanette and Joyce could elicit Cathy's agreement to have it adopted. She insisted that she wanted Jeanette to foster it.

Jeanette and Joyce discussed the possibility, but they reached the conclusion that this arrangement provided no safeguards for the child. They knew that because of Cathy's emotional instability, some time in the future she might during an argument decide to take the child away. At long last, a solution was found – Jeanette would not foster Cathy's baby but she would adopt it. The child would be told in due course who her real mother was and Cathy could visit it at any time.

By the time Cathy was taken to hospital, it was agreed that Jeanette would be the baby's mother. She was called to assist at the birth since the nurses could not control Cathy. When the baby girl arrived, Cathy wanted nothing to do with it. By a cruel stroke of fate, her fears that her child would be born handicapped or deformed were realised. The baby girl had oesophageal atresia, a missing section of the gullet, which made it impossible for food to reach the stomach. Cathy was now even more hysterically determined that she would have nothing to do with the 'monster' she had given birth to.

Jeanette was now convinced that she was meant to take on this new baby. She and Joyce visited her regularly in the hospital every day to feed, bath and cuddle her. She was christened Wendy and the legalities for an adoption order were set in motion. When she was six weeks old, they took her home. Four months later Wendy became Jeanette's first adopted child. When the baby arrived back from the hospital, the other children were thrilled with her, feeling that she belonged to them as much as to Jeanette.

Little Wendy was a pretty baby but prone to serious chest infections due to her condition. It was to be a further eighteen months before an operation could be performed to complete the missing section of pipe that would carry her food from her throat into her stomach. Meanwhile, the surgeon had brought the upper section out through her neck to avoid the liquids getting into her lungs, one of which had already been damaged by her first two feeds. She was fed twice – by mouth and through a tube leading into the lower section of pipe which went directly into her stomach.

The children seemed unperturbed by this far from sightly method of feeding Wendy; but, despite her nursing training, Jeanette was nauseated every time she saw the child's food emerging from its neck. This food was inevitably wasted since it did not go into the baby's stomach, but the motions of sucking, swallowing and tasting had to be gone through so that Wendy could eventually relate the feeling of having had a meal with those of eating or drinking. Often the tube protruding from Wendy's stomach would become detached, and at first Jeanette or Joyce took her back to hospital to have it reinserted. But this was far too time consuming and they quickly learned how to perform the task themselves.

It would have been very easy to have made an invalid of this severely handicapped baby, but Jeanette would not allow it. The children took Wendy's abnormalities totally for granted and as she grew into a toddler, romped and played with her as if she had no pipes or tubes sticking out of her. She was a sunny-nature, happy child and, in some miraculous way, seemed to united them all as one large family.

Jeanette now came upon a suitable, if badly run down, house. She had a series of meetings with the Social Services Department and the housing authorities, who she eventually persuaded to undertake to rewire the house provided she did the other repairs and decorations.

When finally the rewiring had been carried out, but before Jeanette and her family could move in, the owner of the property suddenly appeared on the scene and laid claim to the house. Through an oversight, the lease had not been renewed and legally the local authority had no claim to it. Two hundred and fifty pounds had been spent on rewiring the house for the benefit of the real owner. The Director of the Social Services was beside himself because of the waste.

He ordered all the relevant social workers to remove every one of Jeanette's children from the dilapidated house in Old Ford Road – within a week. The children's social workers descended *en masse* to talk to their various charges, promising unequivocally that they would not obey the order to remove them from Jeanette's care.

Jeanette went with Joyce to see the man in an attempt to reason with him. Had he, she asked, considered the psychological effect his decision to remove the children would have on them? What mattered were the relationships of trust and security Jeanette was establishing between herself and them. Their physical comforts were relatively unimportant.

'You are living in a house which can only be described as dangerous!' the Director pointed out.

'But to break up the family now would present a far greater and longer-lasting danger,' Joyce argued. The man was unmoved. Did Joyce not realise that he had a duty to the public? Public money must not be wasted. The public had rights...

'Jeanette and I have rights. We, too, are members of the public...'

'No, you are simply foster parents...' was his humiliating and irrational reply.

Clearly, the man was not to be reasoned with. Jeanette would have liked to march out of the room but was physically unable to do so. She had developed back trouble and in order to attend the interview in the first place, Joyce had had to bind her into a splint padded with cushions in order that she could move in an upright position. They had arrived well in advance of the meeting in order that she could be got into a chair before the Director appeared in case, realising how bad her back was, he pronounced Jeanette physically unfit to be caring for one child, let alone twelve. Now, walking sideways like a crab and using the wall for support, Jeanette managed to leave the room with Joyce, her feelings of outrage clearly visible on her face.

Jeanette was due to go to Scotland with the children for their annual holiday. Now suddenly the authorization of the allowances for their train fares and accommodation was withdrawn. Furious at this last minute disappointment for the children, Jeanette said she and Joyce would find the money somehow.

First, she telephoned the Chairman of the Social Services Committee in the vain hope that he would override the ruling. He refused to do so and, furthermore, pointed out to Jeanette that Scotland was legally another country, and if she, the children's foster mother, took them out of England, he would have her arrested for kidnapping and charged with abduction.

Although many of Jeanette's friends and contacts both in England and Scotland protested personally to the Director, there was no way round the legal stand that had been taken. Jeanette was forced to tell her family that the holiday was cancelled.

She spent that summer holiday walking the streets in search of an alternative property. At last she found a large, unoccupied house in Mornington Grove, which, she discovered was leased by the local council from the Quakers. One of the conditions attached to the lease was that it must be used for the benefit of the community. The council was therefore breaking the terms of their lease since not only was the house in a state of disrepair, but it was unoccupied and benefitting nobody. Jeanette lost no time in pointing out to the council that they were in breach of the terms of the lease, but they refused to take any action. Undeterred Jeanette went back to the Quakers, and pointed out that she had twelve children urgently in need of a home.

After sending someone round to see the conditions at Old Ford Road, they at once took up the matter with the council. Their actions were effective: the house was allocated to Jeanette with an agreement that the necessary repairs would be done.

That autumn they had added to the Family yet again by taking in Bridget's son Martin on a permanent basis. The Social Services' supervision of the boys had proved inadequate. Neither Martin nor his young brother had been to school for over two years and his social worker discovered belatedly that Martin had been beaten up again and spent a large part of his life locked in his room. At long last, Len had been arrested.

Martin had changed almost beyond recognition. Where once he had been outgoing, even courageous in standing up to the violent man his mother lived with, he was now completely withdrawn. Gradually, Jeanette learned that he had been made the whipping boy for the family conflicts, and was taunted by his mother's cohabitee and by his brothers. His bedroom had become a refuge and he left it only to go to the bathroom. He no longer answered if he was spoken to, and had developed an acute complex about his appearance. Although a nice looking boy, he had been told so often that he was ugly and socially unacceptable, that he had come to believe it.

He presented Jeanette with new problems. Although she insisted that he join the Family at mealtimes, he would neither speak nor look at anyone. When she went to his bedroom where he chose to spend all his time she would find him either washing himself or his clothes, or combing his hair in a pathetic attempt to improve his appearance. She was unable even to elicit a simple 'hello' from him. Remembering the bright, intelligent and friendly little boy she had known in the past, Jeanette felt alternately despairing and doubly determined to reclaim him from the limbo in which he had placed himself.

Cathy meanwhile had returned from Scotland, where Jeanette had sent her to a doctor friend to recuperate after her confinement. When she returned, Jeanette found her a flat and a job as an usherette in a cinema. She would come round quite frequently to Jeanette's house but these visits had very soon to be discouraged. Cathy would regard her child with horror and still refer to her as 'a monster'. Fortunately, the baby was still too young to understand but Jeanette foresaw what it might do to her as she grew older. Moreover, the older children were already aware of Cathy's revulsion for the baby and were both puzzled and resentful. Hardening her heart, Jeanette put severe limits on Cathy's visits.

Christmas that year was a very happy one. As always, Jeanette was determined that her family would enjoy the festivities as much as any other family. She arranged for visits from the children's parents to take place on Christmas Eve or during the few days prior to the holiday since few of the children enjoyed these disturbing reunions. As always she had been buying birthday and Christmas presents with the limited funds at her disposal ever since the January sales at the start of the year, and every child woke on Christmas morning to a stocking with sweets and small toys like colouring pencils or cheap games. The little ones went to bed early on Christmas Eve whilst Jeanette took the older children to the midnight, candle-lit service at the local Methodist Chapel.

Sometimes Joyce's sister, a missionary, would be home from India and would join them for the festivities. Her mother would be present and, until he died, a lonely old man who lived nearby. Somehow, money was found to buy a turkey and after Christmas lunch was cleared away and washed up, the children would be given larger toys obtained by Jeanette through the 'Toys for Children' charity advertised in a newspaper. She or Joyce would go round collecting them all in the week before Christmas. The Methodist minister, Jeanette's friend, always provided toys, as did Spitafields Church and a local Church of England school which had 'adopted' the Family. At harvest time, this school would send all their produce to Jeanette, thus enabling her to save some of the precious housekeeping money for Christmas presents.

The children, too, bought each other presents with money Jeanette set aside to pay for any jobs they did for her; it was specifically hoarded for their Christmas gifts to each other. These tasks began in the summer holidays and saving went on through the autumn until December.

Throughout November and December, Sandra and Luke had maintained their progress; Luke had begun to feed himself and Sandra to show affection to Jeanette and her brother and, if only superficially, had become friendly and outgoing with the other children. The prospects for both children looked promising; but suddenly, one January day, their mother's social worker called to see Jeanette. The children, he informed her, were to be returned to Julie, who now had a 'nice new home' waiting for them.

Jeanette was aghast.

'But they've never met their mother's cohabitee. They've never once seen this "nice new home" they're to go to! You'll have to give them time to establish some kind of relationship with their mother before they leave here. They are far too young to understand what is happening. I need time to prepare them ... take them to see Julie. How long have I got? A couple of months? Six weeks ...?'

The social worker avoided Jeanette's gaze.

He had only once seen Luke and Sandra since they had joined Jeanette's family a year ago and quite readily admitted that he did not like working with children. He had been building up a relationship with their mother and was sympathetic to Julie's desire to have her children returned to her. He was not anxious now to meet any opposition from Jeanette who, he knew very well, had no standing where decisions of this nature were concerned. She was only their foster mother.

'The decision has been made,' he said flatly, 'and with my approval. They are to leave in two days time.'

Chapter 10

'In 1982, the Criminal Justice Act stated that in Juvenile Courts "... the parents can be asked to leave the Court while the child gives evidence..."'
(Harry Tunnicliffe, The Law Says..., *Pepar Publications, 1985)*

The children missed Sandra and her baby brother a great deal. Jeanette not only missed them; she also worried about them constantly. No one gave her news of them and when she asked their social worker for information, she was told that the children were not her concern now that she was no longer fostering them.

Perhaps fortunately, her mind was fully occupied. Mick was still running away, but less frequently. Jeanette wrote his telephone number in the hood of his anorak and asked him to show that he cared a little bit about how worried she was by ringing her to let her know he was all right. She felt a moment of pure joy the first time he did so.

He continued to steal and to be destructive if he was upset. Jeanette expected no less. She had learnt that these emotionally disturbed children needed constantly to put the validity of her caring and concern for them to the test. Their past experiences had instilled in them a deep mistrust of human nature; no one before in their lives had cared about their happiness or well being, and trust was a concept they found difficult to accept. Now Mick was not only reacting in the only way he knew to the emotional disturbances of his mother's visits, but he was

98

discovering how genuine Jeanette was in her desire to help him. On many occasions, Jeanette telephoned his social worker, asking him to call and see the distraught state Mick was in after his mother's visits. Barbara O'Brien was often hysterical, threatening to ram the house with her car or to knife Jeanette. If she ended up in prison as a result of such an action, she told Mick, *he* would be responsible. It was *his* fault she was unhappy. If he cared about her he would tell his social worker he was willing to return home.

Despite the fact that Mick had by now been classified as educationally subnormal, he was intelligent enough to assess the consequences of his mother carrying out her threats to harm Jeanette. With no power to prevent these visits from Barbara and no support from his social worker, Jeanette could do little but cope with the results as Mick trembled, vomited, had terrible nightmares and slept in such a state of tension that he crouched on all four limbs and rocked continuously.

The social worker very rarely responded to Jeanette's calls for him to come and see for himself the damage these maternal visits caused. When he did come, he made the situation even more traumatic, referring to Mick's mother in such a way as to make the boy feel even more guilty that he was responsible for causing her so much worry.

He needed endless reassurance from Jeanette that he could not be held responsible for his mother's problems or the difficulties they caused. But her efforts to stabilise him were undermined always by the attitude of his social worker who, at the statutory six months review of his Care Order, reported to the Court that: 'the needs of the natural family to maintain contact with the boy are imperative and should be encouraged.' The man seemed unable to appreciate that it was this continuing contact that was holding up Mick's progress towards normality.

As a result of the social worker's report, Mick's family were free to continue their pressure on the boy to return home. On one occasion, he gave in to the pressure and returned to his family for four days. Every instinct in Jeanette's body urged her to go and fetch him, but she kept a rigid control of herself. To remove him forcibly from his mother now was to risk seriously antagonising her.

Someone from the Social Services Department tried but failed to retrieve him from his home. As a last resort, Jeanette agreed to the social worker's suggestion that she should collect the boy from the headmaster's study since neither she nor the social worker wished to call in the police.

But as Jeanette had feared, the incident damaged her relationship with Barbara. She now clearly believed that Jeanette was being possessive and was destroying her relationship with her son. She was so strongly involved in an emotional war with Jeanette that in the spring she applied to the Court for the Care Order to be revoked.

Knowing full well that Mick's social worker was still, after a year, unaware of the boy's problems, still less of the progress he had made, Jeanette decided that she could not allow the Court hearing to proceed without Mick being separately represented lest Barbara won her appeal and the Care Order was revoked. Since she herself was not allowed to represent him, she reasoned that he ought to have his own solicitor to put his side of the case. Having established that Mick, a minor, was entitled to be legally represented, she proceeded to argue his rights with the Social Services Department until finally they agreed to her request.

There was nothing she could do, however, to protect the boy from cross-questioning, and Jeanette was far from sure how he would face up to the ordeal of going into a witness box in the solemnity of a Court and answering the questions put to him. It was only fifteen months since he had been no more articulate than a four-year-old. It was not until 1982 that the Criminal Justice Act might have spared Mick the trauma of speaking against his mother, in her presence. As it was, on the day of the hearing he was standing only a few feet away from her when haltingly he told the Court how she had sent him out stealing his own food; that she neither fed him, loved him nor cared about his needs, and that he did not want to go back home.

The Court's decision not to grant Barbara a revocation of the Care Order enraged the unhappy woman, who now felt that her inabilities as a mother had been publicly endorsed. She lost all control and ranted and raved at both Mick and Jeanette, renewing all the boy's feelings of guilt and betrayal. Hardly surprisingly, Mick reverted yet again to many of his old emotional disturbances – nightmares, bed-wetting, sleep-walking. The occasional visits from his social worker only aggravated the situation.

Though pleased with the Court's decision, Jeanette was furiously angry that even now she was not to be given adequate support – in fact the very opposite – from Mick's social worker. She realised that the boy needed someone other than herself to reassure him, to discuss his education with him, to help him come to terms with his future place in society. She herself needed and expected support and reassurance in her handling of the child.*

It was not until the following year that she felt compelled to write a detailed report of Mick's case to an official, condemning their lack of co-operation. Seven pages long, this open letter could not be ignored. Undoubtedly, it caused considerable alarm and the contents were brought speedily to the attention of a Principal Assistant in the Directorate of Social Services.

His brief reply praised the 'courage and tremendous efforts' Jeanette had made in building up a loving, trusting and caring relationship with Mick when she could so easily have rejected him. 'I am aware of the criticism of the social workers concerned,' the letter said, 'but thought that, because of your own extremely high standards of caring, your expectations of what they could contribute may have been too high?' He suggested that at the next review of Mick's case, the subject of Barbara O'Brien's unsettling visits to her son might be discussed.

Jeanette was sickened by the placatory tone of the letter and the implication that her own standards were unnecessarily high. Moreover, it made no admission that the social worker had failed both her and – far more importantly – the child whose welfare was his responsibility. Although she was convinced that

---

*Boarding Out Regulations, 1955; amended by Boarding out of Children Regulations, 1982. Long term fostering: A local authority or voluntary agency which has arranged the boarding out of a child shall ensure that a visitor sees the child and visits the dwelling of the foster parents ... once in every six weeks if the child has not attained the age of five years, or if he has attained that age, once in every two months. (H. Tunnicliffe, *The Law Says . . .*, Pepar Publications, 1985)

her report had been a waste of time and effort, it had wider repercussions than the Principal Assistant's reply had led her to anticipate. At the next review of Mick's case, Barbara O'Brien's visits to her son were curtailed.

The subsequent decrease in the frequency of Barbara's visits to Mick had the desired effect. He began to attend school regularly, to concentrate more easily and he no longer thought of running way. The other children rallied round him in bad moments. In particular Tom, who at the age of twelve was only a year younger than Mick, befriended him. Tom had grown into a delightful youngster with a placid, sunny disposition. He enjoyed scout camping expeditions to the full and derived the maximum benefit from his schooling. Like Robbie, he was a member of the local army cadet corps. He was a pleasure to have around and the realisation of how far he had come since those early years when, frightened and abused, he had exhibited all the usual behaviour problems, gave Jeanette renewed confidence in Mick's gradual progress. Unaware of what lay in store, she felt every reason to be hopeful for the future.

In April at long last the Family finally moved to the Mornington Grove house but before they were able to do so, squatters beat them to it. 'This is a demonstration,' said a large, burly fellow confronting her in the doorway. 'We're sociology students *and we're staying*.' Jeanette was not intimidated.

'Then we'll all move in with you!' she stated firmly.

'Who's "all"?'

'Me, my friend Joyce and the kids – Robbie, Joan, Tom, Gary, Ellen, Natalie, Martin, Mick, Catrina, Simon and the baby, Wendy...'

'In that case, we move out!' the student said, acknowledging defeat with a grin.

Although there were two adults and eleven children crowded into the five-bedroomed house, Jeanette was suddenly approached by the Social Services Department with a request to have Sandra and Luke returned to her. She was not entirely surprised since she had learned from other sources that their mother, Julie, had been unable to cope with them; that she was pregnant again and anxious that the two children should be sent back to Jeanette.

She was soon to discover why the Social Services Department were only too pleased to put Luke and Sandra back in her care despite their social worker's attitude. Both children had regressed to a shocking degree in the six months since they had left her.

Luke had once again to be spoon-fed, and to be put back in nappies. He had reverted to his habit of withdrawal from contact with the other children and remained motionless for hours on end unless someone physically removed him from his chosen position in a corner of the room. He was once again afraid of being bathed and did not react to sound or pain. Once, when he caught his finger in a door and had to have the nail removed, he gave no indication of the pain it caused. Sandra, too, was severely emotionally disturbed and both children again had terrible sores on their bodies caused by lying for hours on wet bedding or by being left in wet or soiled clothes.

Slowly, painstakingly, Jeanette began the task of rebuilding all that had been undone and gradually, over the next three months, the children's mental and physical condition began to improve again. Now Luke would not let Jeanette out of his sight and followed her from room to room. Unbelievably, in the September of that year, without prior warning or consultation with Jeanette, both children were yet again returned to their mother – despite the fact that Julie now had her new baby to contend with as well as her former psychopathic husband who was abusing her. In less than three months, Julie again took refuge in the battered wives' hostel and by November, the children were once more back with Jeanette.

The damage done to Luke during that second removal from Jeanette's care was immense. Somewhere in the recesses of his two-year-old brain, he must have realised that he could not trust in the permanence of his place of safety or the continued presence and loving care of the woman who mothered him. He returned to Jeanette with no control over his bladder or bowels, seemingly unaware of the physical acts of voidance. Far more distressingly to Jeanette, he now appeared to cut himself off from her completely. If he was not fed, he would not eat. If he was put to bed, he would simply stay there – for ever, Jeanette told herself wretchedly – if he were not lifted out.

Jeanette's despair was absolute – but with her characteristic tenacity, courage and faith, for the third time she began the seemingly impossible task of trying to reach the children with her love. At the back of her mind there was always the fear that their social worker might once more persuade the local authority to allow their mother to have them back.

Julie came to visit the children – always an unsettling occasion for them – but although she professed an interest in their progress, Jeanette knew that her prime need was for mothering for herself. She demanded from Jeanette constant reassurance because of the guilt she felt at her inability to manage her life and her children. She was as much a child as they, emotionally immature as a result of her own inadequate upbringing. Jeanette did what she could to reassure and counsel her, grateful that Julie showed no sign of wanting Luke and Sandra home again.

Two case conferences took place, one in March and one in September. By then, the hospital where Jeanette had to take the children for assessment of their condition had discovered that Luke had muscle hypotonia requiring weekly physiotherapy; and that Sandra had a damaged kidney needing further investigation. It was suggested at the September case conference and agreed by all the agencies present that the children's social worker should apply for rights and powers to safeguard the children's future. Since the social worker was only a junior, he could do no more than agree to discuss the recommendation with his supervisor.

Jeanette now had reason to be hopeful that the children's gradual progress was not to be disrupted again. That hope was unfounded. A year after their third placement with her, their social worker suddenly telephoned to tell her that Sandra and Luke were once again to be returned to their mother, who wanted them home by Christmas. At first, Jeanette could not believe what she was being told. The Department knew that each time the children had been brought back from their mother, it had taken her longer to get through to them, to redress the damage done.

'You're not having them!' she said emphatically. 'I refuse point blank to let them go!'

The social worker felt on safe ground.

104

'The children are with you only on a Voluntary Care Order. Their mother is entitled to ask for them back whenever she wishes.'

'I'm not interested in their mother's wishes. At the last case conference, everyone agreed that their future needed to be made secure.' Jeanette tried to keep her voice level as she added furiously: 'Julie has three other children now, and I am not prepared to let Luke and Sandra go back to her. If they are still on a Voluntary Care Order, that is your problem and you'd better sort it out.'

There was now a statutory month before the children could be removed from Jeanette's care. During that month, a case conference was held and a new social worker telephoned to ask if he could come round to discuss the children's future with her. She agreed to the discussion provided it was understood that Luke and Sandra were not leaving her.

For one long afternoon, Jeanette and the social worker talked. At last she had found someone who understood the situation and who was willing to do what he could to persuade his superiors to support her. Finally convinced, the Social Services took the matter to the local Court, and had parental rights transferred to the local authority.

On the night before the Court hearing, Julie rang Jeanette to ask if it was her intention to tell the whole story from the beginning. She was receiving advice from a local solicitor. When Jeanette told her that for the children's sake she intended to hold nothing back from the Court, Julie said hopelessly:

'Then I don't stand a chance.'

'But the children will . . .' Jeanette had replied.

After the Court hearing, they were placed with Jeanette on a Permanent Care Order. For Luke and Sandra's sake, Jeanette could not afford to feel sorry for their mother. Julie was now associating with a married man who was suspected of being involved with drugs, and she had been sharing a flat with Catrina and Simon's mother who had recently died in highly suspicious circumstances. The woman had fallen from the balcony of the flat on to some railings and had not died immediately. Someone had been arrested and charged with her murder but there was insufficient proof for a conviction.

Clearly, the environment was totally unsuitable for Luke and Sandra, and the Social Services Department knew it because Julie's other two children were on the 'At Risk' register.

Mercifully Catrina had been away at guide camp at the time of the tragedy so was not so deeply affected by her mother's bizarre death as was her brother, Simon. He withdrew completely and Jeanette could not reach him. She realised he needed help, and telephoned the Social Services Department to ask for their support. It was some while before her call was returned. The Department could not allocate Simon a social worker, but they would be willing to give the boy money for mourning clothes. Jeanette's disgust knew no bounds. Simon himself sat down and wrote a sad little poem that he entitled '*I think I've been forgotten.*'

Meanwhile Jeanette had a new problem on her hands. She had been approached by the Parents for Children adoption agency. They were at their wits' end to know where to place a family of four children, three of them fostered and one mentally handicapped, while their parents took a week's holiday to sort out their problems. Jeanette agreed to take the children. By now, the large attic of the Mornington Grove house had been turned into a bedroom and the sitting-room partitioned into three small bedrooms, so somehow – for a week – they would manage.

That week was to provide Jeanette with her first introduction to the terrible additional problems facing a mentally retarded, unwanted child. At the age of fourteen, Sylvie McGuire had experienced rejection eight times. Abandoned at birth, she had spent the first seven years of her life in a residential nursery before finding her first foster home. Sylvie was one of two handicapped children. This placement, like all the others that followed, had not lasted: when the foster mother had died unexpectedly, her daughter kept one child but did not feel she could look after two. Sylvie had been sent away to a Children's Home. Because of her education difficulties, there were moves to other Children's Homes, one of which was forced to close down. All the other children were rehoused together but once again, because of her special needs, Sylvie was sent somewhere different. The attempts by her devoted social worker to find her a permanent foster home were never successful. Now, it seemed as if her present placement with a family who intended to adopt her was breaking down due to the refusal of the other children in the family to accept her.

Jeanette had become accustomed to the frequent cruelty of adults towards children but now she was horrified to discover how immensely cruel children could be to each other. Embarrassed by Sylvie's odd, childish behaviour, which was frequently expressed in uncontrolled screaming tantrums, they threatened her constantly with the possibility that their parents would get rid of her. From the time Sylvie got up in the morning to the time she went to bed, one or other of them was always downing her, teasing and tormenting her or warning her that if she were not better behaved, nobody would like her or want her near them; that she looked silly, was silly. Jeanette's nerves were frayed to breaking point and the other children in the Family were shocked and bewildered by the degree of dislike Sylvie's 'siblings' showed towards her.

Sylvie's reactions were predictable. Afraid of being rejected by the family she had hoped would be a permanent one at long last, she dared not retaliate against her tormentors. Driven to breaking point, she would lose control and scream hysterically or else ill-treat the family pets, kicking the puppy, which at other times she clearly adored.

It came as no surprise to Jeanette when the parents telephoned her to say that when they came to collect the other children, they did not wish to take Sylvie home with them. They insisted that although personally they were fond of her and felt sorry for her, they had decided that her behaviour disturbed the other children. Sylvie was therefore to find herself unwanted yet again. Her social worker promised Jeanette she would do what she could to find new foster parents for the unhappy girl whilst Jeanette agreed that *she* would do what *she* could to persuade Sylvie that the decision not to return to her foster family was her own choice and not because of *their* rejection of *her*.

It was not an easy task. Events covering Sylvie's separation from her foster family had happened too fast for her to be properly prepared for the change. Whilst admitting that she hated the children in the family, Sylvie was convinced that she

107

herself was to blame for their dislike of her. With the mental age of a much younger child, verbally incoherent and able to sense her 'difference' from other children, Sylvie was bewildered and very frightened. Despite her social worker's promise to find her a new family, she anticipated that inevitably they, too, would turn against her because she did not behave properly. Her confusion resulted in her trying to drown the kitten in the bath and strangle the puppy with a rope. She cried continuously. Her pain and fear was such that there were moments when Jeanette herself could not bear it and had to remove herself to a quiet corner to get away from the child's suffering.

Sylvie's distress was heartbreaking and Jeanette decided to take her on holiday to Scotland since the only other alternatives were for the girl to be returned to a Children's Home or sent to a reception centre for psychiatric assessment. It was during her brief holiday that Jeanette decided Sylvie must not be left uncertain even where, or with whom, she would spend Christmas. She told Sylvie's social worker that they would keep her with them until after the Christmas holiday. Grateful for the extra time this gave them, the Parents for Children agency promised to do their best to find a permanent home for the girl.

Jeanette now reached the conclusion that because of her inarticulate speech the girl had appeared more handicapped than she was. She spoke a great deal more clearly now and during the holiday one of Jeanette's friends had successfully taught her to knit. She had become less hysterical and was gentle and loving with the younger children in the Family. Despite the cruelty which older children had previously exhibited towards her, she was the one who worried most if one of Jeanette's family was late back from school or in distress. Intensely affectionate, sometimes overly so toward the other girls, she gave love to everyone and the children had become fond of her.

Jeanette spent a great deal of time talking to her, attempting to reassure her that although, as Sylvie so often despaired, she was not quite like the other children, she did have special gifts of her own, such as her exceptional sensitivity to the feelings and needs of other people. In this atmosphere, in which no one in the Family was ever allowed to be deliberately unkind to anyone else, Sylvie began to blossom.

Soon after Christmas, Margaret, Sylvie's devoted social worker in whose care she had been since she was a little girl, came round to see Jeanette. Despite all the countless efforts Margaret had made to find Sylvie a home, only a Catholic Children's Home for the Mentally Handicapped, run by nuns, was prepared to consider taking her.

Jeanette looked at Margaret aghast.

'But that isn't the right place for Sylvie!' she said. 'She can't go there! *You* don't think it's right, do you?'

The social worker shook her head.

'It's very far from ideal, but we simply can't find anything better,' was Margaret's blunt reply.

'Then Sylvie stays here with us,' Jeanette stated flatly.

Margaret smiled. She had known Jeanette for a long while and had anticipated this reaction.

As soon as the authorities heard that Sylvie was to become a permanent resident, an official telephoned Jeanette to say that the Social Services Department would not permit it; that there were to be no more children in the house.

'So what am I supposed to do with the child?' Jeanette asked bluntly.

'You'll just have to put her out,' was the reply. 'Turn her on to the street.'

'You can't be serious!' Jeanette said incredulously.

'I mean what I say. The police will pick her up and then she won't be your responsibility.'

Jeanette put down the telephone, too angry for further speech. Perhaps the worst of her anger lay in her knowledge that this was no bluff. To the authorities, Sylvie was not a human being, a child – she was merely an unwelcome statistic.

She turned to look at the plain, adolescent waif playing contentedly on the floor with the baby, Wendy.

'Sylvie's part of the Family now,' she thought, her mouth set in a determined line, 'and so long as I live, she's never, *ever* going to be abandoned again!'

Despite her brave thoughts, a slight shiver of apprehension went through her. The last time the Health Visitor had called in, she had pointed out that Jeanette was breaking the rules by keeping so many children in the small house. Without doubt the authorities were only too well aware that in addition to Sylvie she had recently taken on yet another child.

Chapter 11

'Study after study, both here and abroad, has shown that the overwhelming majority of abusing parents are ignorant of elementary facts of child rearing...'
(*Vida Carver,* Child abuse, a study text, *Open University Press, 1978*)

The ten-year-old new newcomer, Jason, had been moved no less than eighteen times prior to one of the adoption agency's request to Jeanette that she should take him into her Family. He had been shunted to and from Children's Homes, his own home and various foster homes. Jeanette went to see him.

He was an attractive little boy with his Spanish mother's dark eyes, olive skin and dark curly hair. He was very quiet whilst the house-parent escorted her round the Children's Home, but once they were left alone to have lunch together in the staff flat, he seemed anxious to talk. She sensed that he was confused by very mixed emotions, wanting to welcome her and yet needing to reject her, perhaps before she could reject him.

It was common practice for every child placed in a Children's Home to keep an album containing a personal record of their life. It might contain photographs of the child himself or of his relatives, school reports, records of his achievements –in fact any data that might assist a child to recognise his own identity and remember his roots. Jason produced his book eagerly and, quickly turning over the first page on which was his birth certificate, pointed to the next page.

'You ought to look at that,' he commented. 'It's important!'

'Do you want to talk about it?' Jeanette asked.

He hesitated before replying, 'That's my Mum. She'll always be my Mum. You won't ever take her place . . .'

Jeanette thought for a moment before she replied softly:

'I don't want to take her place, Jason. But I do want – and am determined – to have a place of my own.'

The child's eyes filled with tears as he continued to turn the pages of his book, showing her the photographs of himself with other children he had been with at this and other Homes.

Several times that afternoon he repeated his statement about his mother. It was as if he needed Jeanette's repeated reply that it was not her intention to replace his mother, but to care about him as a mother. Most of the time, however, he spent informing her how clever he was. It was impossible, he stated, that any of the children in Jeanette's family could possibly be as clever as he was.

Jeanette quickly realised that this would not be an easy child to handle. Her first visit was followed by a second when she and young Tom took him out to lunch and to do some shopping. He behaved quite appallingly on the underground, shouting, swearing and jumping on the seats, upsetting the window display in one of the shops and demanding to be given anything which took his fancy. His aquisitiveness was perhaps the most severe symptom he showed of emotional disturbance.

A weekend visit to Jeanette's home was arranged. No sooner had he arrived than he demanded to be given the other children's possessions, refusing to take no for an answer. Tom, always a sensitive, gentle boy, offered to share his toys but Jason was not interested in sharing. He refused to eat the food offered him, declaring that he was allowed to have whatever took his fancy at the Childrens Home. He religiously went through any visitor's handbag and took what he wanted from it. When Jeanette took some of the children with Jason to the market to buy Christmas presents, he spent the whole time begging, pleading, bribing to be given sweets, toys, ornaments. When Jeanette reiterated that he had fifty pence to spend on himself and that he was getting nothing more, he declared sullenly:

'I don't like you!'

But when the time came for her to take him back to the

Children's Home and he packed his few belongings, he left behind the small blanket which, he had told her, his mother had given him when he was taken away from her as a little boy. It was clear then to Jeanette that he had decided that he wanted to live with them on a permanent basis.

When the day came for Jason to leave the Home, he seemed indifferent to his parting from his friends and house parents. On arrival at Jeanette's house, he went up to his room to unpack, first placing some of his paper models on top of the television set. Jeanette warned him they would not be safe there from the younger children, but he ignored her. When he came down from his room, the baby, Wendy, was reaching for the models. As Jason started shouting and screaming at her to leave his things alone, the child burst into tears.

Jeanette reminded him that it was his own fault they had been at risk.

'She shouldn't touch them – you shouldn't let her,' he shouted.

'Please don't shout at me like that and don't shout at the baby!' Jeanette replied firmly.

His dark eyes glared at her.

'I will shout at her if she touches my stuff!'

Jeanette returned his gaze.

'I've asked you not to shout at me or the baby. Now put your things in your room!'

The boy's bravado crumpled. He looked suddenly very frightened and said frantically, 'I'm sorry, I'm sorry! I didn't mean to shout at her!'

Hating to see the fear in the child's eyes, yet knowing she must remain firm, Jeanette said gently, 'That's all right. Just put your models in your room, love.'

She made to leave the room but Jason followed her.

'Are you going to send me back . . . ?'

Jeanette knelt down beside him.

'No, Jason. And you should realise that in the next few weeks and months, you are going to do lots more things to make me cross – all parents get cross with their children sometimes.'

'I won't do anything wrong again!' he said frantically.

'I expect you will – all children do and I shall be cross with

113

you – but it doesn't mean I intend to send you back to the Home. You will hear me being cross with all the children, but this is their home just as it's now your home. It's what family life is all about, Jason, loving and trusting each other, and caring and discipline. It won't be easy for you and you may feel frightened at times.'

'I don't care so long as you don't send me back. I want to live here. I'm sorry – I'm *sorry* I shouted!'

'You'll probably shout again,' Jeanette said, 'but it's got nothing to do with you living here.'

The boy's arms lifted as if he were on the point of putting them around Jeanette's neck; but he stopped himself just in time. Abruptly he turned away from her and sauntered off into the sitting room. Jeanette despatched one of the other boys to keep him company, believing as she did that no emotionally disturbed child should be left alone unless they wished it. As she went to the kitchen to make herself a cup of coffee, Jeanette realised that it would be a long time yet before Jason learned to trust her reassurances that he would never be rejected again.

There was a certain irony in the way he clung to the memory of his mother. There had been occasional moments when the woman had shown him an affection which he had never forgotten, but frequently she had left him and her two other children for days on end. One day, she had shut them in a room with a small amount of food and water and forbidden them to go out until she returned. At the end of the third day, little Jason had decided to leave the room to ask a neighbour for help. As a result, the neighbour telephoned the Social Services Department. Jason was blamed and his furious mother had attacked him with a broom handle, splitting open the side of his head.

Jeanette had seen the scar. Now that she was getting to know him, she wondered how many other scars he had – unseen, emotional scars inflicted by the mother he still remembered with love.

Luke, his sister Sandra, and the twins were making steady progress although one of the twins, Ellen, was suffering the consequences of living so near to her natural family. One day she found her sisters waiting by the gates of her school. Despite her

114

screams of protest, they forcibly dragged her back to their house with them.

Although on that occasion Jeanette was able to take Ellen safely back to her own home with the assistance of a friendly policeman, she was fearful lest there might be similar incidents in future. There was nothing she could do to stop Mrs Cook's repeated visits to the house, usually when she was in a drunken state, always at Christmas time and on the twins' birthday. All too frequently, she would accost Jeanette and the twins in the street when they were out shopping and cause a scene. In a drunken maudlin voice, she would give free rein to her emotions.

''Ow's me little darlin's, me precious babies? I want me babies back – give me back me little angels!'

The children would cling closer to Jeanette, avoiding their mother's hysterical attempts to embrace them, and for several days afterwards they would be distressed and difficult.

Fortunately, there were no such problems with Robbie's mother, Mary, with whom Jeanette had managed to retain a good relationship. Robbie had recently won a Scout award – the youngest boy in the district ever to receive this particular honour. He was hoping eventually to join the army. Joan, his elder sister, had already left home and was in her own flat. She had obtained a good job as an assistant in a nursery and had met someone she hoped soon to marry.

Joan had obtained her flat through the goodwill of Jeanette's friend, Ken Start, who was Director of a Christian charitable organisation called the Springboard Housing Association. She had met him on a number of occasions at meetings of the National Children's Homes Committee of which they were both members. Ken had spent many a long hour at Mornington Grove discussing with Jeanette the repairs that were necessary and ensuring that they were properly carried out. He had the Family's interests very much at heart. Ken now told her of two large, adjoining houses in Campbell Road, numbers 21 and 23, which he thought it might be possible for them to rent. He was able to arrange for the Family to lease both premises as soon as they could be converted into one dwelling. In the meanwhile, Jeanette would be allowed access to number 23.

Jeanette was at first delighted with this unexpected solution to their housing problems. She would have been horrified had she realised that it was to be a further four years before the other house was acquired by the Family. No one had thought to inform the Housing Association that the Campbell Road properties were to be occupied by a family – albeit a large one. It was therefore assumed that the premises were to be turned into a Children's Home. The regulations for such a change of tenancy required a notice to be pinned up on the door of one of the houses announcing the change to give the local residents the opportunity to object if they so wished. Doubtless envisaging a hoard of delinquent children arriving to disrupt the peace and quiet of their neighbourhood, the Tenants' Association promptly got up a petition objecting to the proposal and sent it to the local authority.

This misfortune was compounded when the local authority Social Services went on strike, thus causing endless delays to the committee meetings dealing with, among other things, the Campbell Road problems.

'We shall just have to try to be patient!' Jeanette said as she continued to struggle with the daily difficulties of their small, overcrowded house in Mornington Grove.

They did, however, take formal possession of number 23 immediately, recognising the danger that squatters would otherwise move in. This had an unsettling effect upon Sylvie, who became convinced that when the Family moved in, she would be left behind. To reassure her, Jeanette allowed her first to choose a bedroom and a carpet, and then to store some of her possessions there.

Sylvie was slowly adjusting to her new life with the Family. Although she still had difficulty in expressing her feelings in words, there were times when she could be perfectly articulate. When she had first gone to live with Jeanette on a Permanent Foster Care order, her educational assessment had been transferred to the local borough. They automatically allocated her a place at a school similar to the one she had previously attended, namely a school for severely subnormal children who were considered to be uneducable.

Jeanette took Sylvie to inspect the school and realised

immediately that this was not the right environment for the girl. Many of the children were so retarded that they could not even feed themselves. It could only be a retrograde step for Sylvie to be amongst children far more seriously mentally handicapped than she was. Sylvie herself was very far from enthusiastic about going there. She had spent the last ten years in schools just like it, she told Jeanette, and had no wish to go to another one.

Jeanette's decision to keep Sylvie at home until a more appropriate school was found for her infuriated the education authorities. Did Jeanette realise, they enquired, that she could be sent to prison for failing to send Sylvie to school? Jeanette ignored the implied threat. Fortunately, she had the whole-hearted support of Margaret Kaye, Sylvie's social worker. Together, the three attended an interview with the Inspector of Education at the County Hall.

Invited to put her case, Jeanette pointed out that Sylvie was well capable of normal behaviour in a number of respects. She could do the shopping if the list were not too complicated; she could look after the little ones provided she was supervised; she was helpful and able with the housework.

'So you think you can do my job better than I can?' enquired her inquisitor sarcastically.

Jeanette replied coldly that it was possible for people like him to make mistakes and one of them was now sitting in front of him; if he talked to Sylvie he would quickly discover that for himself.

Believing the man was genuinely interested in her, Sylvie responded happily and eloquently to his subsequent questions.

'Do you like cooking, Sylvie?'

'Yer, what do *you* like doing?'

'I like playing football.'

'I don't – it's too rough. What d'yer want to know all these things for?'

'I want to know what sort of school you should go to!'

'Not the sort you've sent me to!' was Sylvie's truthful reply. Jeanette and Margaret were trying to hide their smiles as Sylvie rattled on. 'They're for stupid people and I'm not stupid. They can't think and I can think. I do the housework and the cooking. I do everything at home.'

117

At the end of an hour, it was perfectly clear that Sylvie's mental handicap was not classifiable as 'severe' and that her cheerful and articulate replies to his questions had actually charmed the Inspector. Sylvie won her own victory. The Inspector conceded that she should be given a short trial at an alternative school for children who were only educationally subnormal.*

That summer was a particularly happy one for all the Family. Jeanette, Joyce, her mother and the fourteen children were offered holiday accommodation in a farmhouse in Coolham, Sussex, by a friend they had made during one of their Scottish holidays. The house was owned by the Christian St Julian's Community, of which their friend was a member.

The farm was large enough to house them all. They were able for the whole of that summer holiday to escape from the dusty confines of the London streets and run free in the fields and lanes, to feed the farm animals, to picnic out of doors. The older children went for bicycle rides, went fishing for tiddlers in the streams and ponds, built camps for the little ones to play in, watched the milking in a nearby dairy farm.

For six whole weeks, they were free from the intervention of their natural families; free to feel as an integral part of nature; and, not least of all, they were able to enjoy the harmless pleasures of a country child.

* This type of school is now termed a School for Children with Special Needs and Learning Difficulties.

Chapter 12

'... "homo ferus" (wolf child) is devoid of
human attributes such as affection, laughter,
normal emotions... is mute except when he
growls, grunts or howls in wolf like outbursts.
While incapable of living like a human being he
exists like an animal...' Scientific definition.
(Basil Copper, Werewolf in Legend, Fact and
Art, Robert Hale, 1977)

It was a bitterly cold December morning when a senior social
worker rang the doorbell of a flat in East London in answer to
an urgent telephone call for assistance from the Jamaican girl
living there. The girl had given no explanation for her request
for immediate help but the social worker was filled with
anxiety. There had been numerous complaints by the
neighbours of sounds of a crying child coming from the flat, and
the police had also received reports of a neglected child. A police
constable had called to investigate, but had seen an infant asleep
in the arms of a young woman and had assumed that there was
no cause for concern.

Nonetheless, the social worker now waiting for the door to
be opened was apprehensive. He had discovered that the four-
year-old boy at this address was on their 'At Risk' register. The
records showed that a health visitor had stated that the child
could not walk properly at the age of fourteen months and had
arranged for him to attend a day nursery. After one visit, the
child had not returned and the Social Services Department had
lost sight of him. This was in part because there had been a
strike by the social workers and in part because the health

visitor, having reported her concern, passed on the responsibility for visiting the boy and counselling his mother to the social workers. There was no record of anyone visiting the mother or child for the past two and a half years.

As the door of the flat was finally opened, the Social Worker's sense of foreboding gave way to horror. Filth littered the floor of the room, the rubbish knee-high. In the centre of it lay the body of a newly born child. Now the social worker understood why the voice on the end of the telephone had insisted that the matter was urgent. He waded through the litter, quickly covered the new-born infant with his coat and hastened out to the telephone kiosk to ring for an ambulance and the police.

The constable who arrived gazed with equal horror at the scene. The stench coming from the two-foot-high piles of rubbish surrounding the only two pieces of furniture in the room – a table and chair – was so nauseating that he had to go outside to vomit. He steeled himself to return. The social worker was doing what he could to help the mother.

As he was about to carry the baby out to the waiting ambulance, he heard a strange noise coming from an adjoining room. Believing it to be a dog or cat shut in there, he opened the door. In the far corner of the room was a cot, and in it was a child curled up in a foetal position. It quickly hid itself beneath a filthy cover as soon as it became aware of his presence. In this room too, the litter reached as high as the window sill and the appalling smell was as bad as – if not worse than – in the front room.

Clearly unused to the sight of any human being other than his mother, the boy was like a terrified wild animal, at first trying to burrow under the mattress and then screeching in a high unearthly note and savagely biting anyone who tried to touch him. It took the two ambulance men and the police constable to remove the child from his cot and carry him out to the vehicle.

Jeanette was asked to go and see the boy the day after his admission to the children's ward of the London Hospital. By now she was on christian name terms with the child psychiatrist, Stephen Wolkind, with whom she had co-operated in the past. They had liaised frequently over the treatment for

Gary and Ellen, and as a consequence, he had acquired a healthy respect for Jeanette. It was he who had asked a senior staff nurse to contact her.

'The boy will certainly die if he remains in the ward,' he had explained when she arrived at the hospital. 'I'll take you to see him, Jeanette. He's being described as a "wolf child", but I personally would describe him as being more like a monkey. As far as I know, there have only ever been four reported cases on medical record in Great Britain.'

Jeanette's nursing studies had certainly not included this particular category of human deprivation. She discovered that 'wolf children' were so called because the earliest recorded cases were of children reared without contact with their fellow human beings, usually by wolves but sometimes by other wild animals. Since they could neither speak nor understand speech, they were often thought to be deaf mutes or mentally deranged. Understandably, these children feared human contact. They reacted like any wild animal, walking on all fours or climbing like monkeys, eating only food that was familiar to their wild state. Since this child had had to survive for almost five years in the solitary confines of his cot, he manifested many of these typical characteristics.

Jeanette understood the definition when she saw the small scrap of humanity crouching in a corner of the hospital cot. The nurses had obviously tried to tidy the boy's long, matted hair, but they had only succeeded in tying it in bunches. Because of his paranoic fear of anyone and everything around him, it had taken the combined efforts of four nurses to bath him. He made terrified noises when anyone approached the cot. Jeanette found it almost impossible to believe that the tiny skeletal figure was that of a child nearly five years old; he would, she thought painfully, fit into a two-year-old's sleeping suit! But despite his size and condition, he fought savagely when a nurse tried to touch him, biting with the small milk teeth which had become grotesquely twisted.

'To all intents and purposes, he is a small, wild animal and reacting like one,' the psychiatrist said to Jeanette. 'He is, of course, shockingly undernourished. We're doing what we can, but I'm convinced that there is no hope of survival for him if he

121

stays here in hospital. It's all too frightening – the noises, the nurses, the doctors, the movement, even the lights. He won't eat or drink. You can see for yourself the rate of his heartbeat. It we keep him here and try to treat him, he will quite literally die of fright. It's doubtful whether he can survive *anywhere* – but he just might have a chance with you. His name is Jasper, by the way.'

Somehow, they managed to wrap the child in a blanket and carry him out to the car. Jeanette held him as best she could whilst Joyce drove them home. By the time they arrived, her arms and hands were covered in bites, all of which were to turn septic. They put him on the settee in the sitting-room. At once, he burrowed under the blanket, and the piercing screeches that had accompanied them on the drive home were temporarily silenced.

Day by day, Jeanette discovered further explanations for little Jasper's condition. He rejected all normal food, eating only rice and drinking only cans of Coca-Cola, his former staple diet. Cutlery or a drinking vessel were unknown to him. Because of his fear of water, Jeanette made no attempt to wash his matted hair, but with Joyce's assistance and ignoring the bites they received, they managed to cut it off. The huge, dark eyes never lost their expression of fear, yet withal he was a surprisingly beautiful child.

Very gradually, the boy's fear became less acute and with their nursing training, Jeanette and Joyce were able to improve his physical health. He never left the sitting-room, remaining for the most part on the settee, which had obviously become for him the same refuge as the cot he had lived in for the past four and a half years. Since there was nothing they could do as yet to toilet-train him, the stench in the room made living conditions nearly unbearable, despite the fact that they kept the window permanently open. He was terrified of the floor, the huge expanse of space unfamiliar to him. If put there, he would lurch crabwise, clinging on to the nearest object, doubtless the only motions available to him in his cot.

Jeanette now learned the little the Social Services Department knew about Jasper's background. His fifteen-year-old mother had come to England from the West Indies to join her

122

parents. But whilst she was on her way to England, her mother had died in a fire. When her father remarried, the girl did not get on with her new stepmother, and since by now she was pregnant, she had been allocated a flat. It was there that Jasper, and now – four and a half years later – the new baby, had been born.

Whilst Jeanette and Joyce struggled to ensure Jasper's survival, their family life continued. Shortly after Christmas, Robbie, her first foster child, decided to change his surname by Deed Poll. He was leaving to join the army and wanted to be registered as Robbie Roberts.

Robbie's 'disappearance' was beyond Sylvie's comprehension. She could not be comforted until Robbie reappeared on his first leave, which reassured her that he had not gone away for ever. But she was far from happy, worrying continually about her 'difference' from other children. Joan and Larry had produced their first child, a little boy called Andrew, who Joan often brought round to the house. The baby had a perfectly normal pressure lump on its head, which greatly worried Sylvie. She would gaze in wonderment at the tiny hands and feet, comparing them with her own; but her expression became tense each time her eyes went to the baby's head.

Finally one night, Jeanette found Sylvie crying in her bedroom. She told Jeanette that she was afraid the baby was going to be 'wrong in the head' like herself, that he would grow up to suffer the same cruel jibes she had so often received from children at school and from thoughtless adults. Only the previous day, when she had been in the launderette helping Jeanette to fold the clean clothes and to stack them in the wash basket, a woman nearby had censured Jeanette.

'People like you who have spastics shouldn't be allowed in places like this!'

Angered by such thoughtless cruelty and the effect it had on children like Sylvie, Jeanette wondered whether she would ever succeed in building up Sylvie's self-confidence; whether, as a family, they could make up to her for the pain she suffered. She now told Jeanette of some of the taunts she had endured at the hands of her previous family and how frightened she had been.

123

'If my mother had loved me when I was born and I had lived with her, would I be all right?' she asked Jeanette, staring at herself in the mirror. Jeanette said what she could to comfort Sylvie. She gave her a tape recorder into which Sylvie poured out her thoughts and feelings. For a long time, she had been upset whenever she heard the other children arguing or quarrelling, but now she rationalised the situation of her own accord. When Sylvie was proudly playing back one of her own recordings, Jeanette was reassured to hear the child's voice saying: 'They're not really arguing – they're just playing!'

Sylvie spent a great deal of time with the little ones, telling them stories that she would tape and later play back to herself so that she could improve upon them. She taped her feelings about the proposed move to the new house; her fears of being left behind were silly, she told some imaginary person, because she had her own room and this was how it was decorated and furnished. Often Jeanette would find her fast asleep at night with the tape recorder still running.

It was difficult not to be over-indulgent with Sylvie; her progress was so gradual they all underestimated the degree of her understanding. Jeanette noticed that Sylvie was getting away with far more than she should, simply by pretending that she had not understood what was asked of her. She was particularly remiss in matters of hygiene and it was a constant battle to get her to wash herself and to wear clean clothes. Although she now knew it was 'wrong', she still on occasions demonstrated her sexual feelings with the animals. Nevertheless, she was making a conscious effort to curb her tendency mainly because she wanted to please everyone around her. Occasionally, she was quite deliberately naughty – mischievously so since she was developing a strong sense of humour. But for both Jeanette and the children there remained the problem of assessing how much was genuinely beyond Sylvie's comprehension.

The advent of Jasper brought new traumas for Sylvie. Because he could neither walk nor talk, she saw him too as 'damaged in his head' and was afraid that he would suffer as she had. Again and again, Jeanette heard her telling the little boy, 'I'll love you even if nobody else loves you. I'll help you...'

Deeply concerned about him, Sylvie wanted always to be

with him. When Jeanette and Joyce attempted to bath Jasper and he was screaming hysterically in fear, Sylvie stood by, doing her best to comfort him.

'Nobody's going to hurt you! Mum says you've got to be clean so's you don't get sore...'

His progress, although painfully slow, was in part a reassurance to her.

But that spring, Jasper developed measles. He had not been immunised as a baby and physically he had almost no reserves to resist the disease. By now, Jeanette could handle him – although no one else could – and for a few days she attempted to nurse him. But his condition rapidly deteriorated and she telephoned the hospital late one night. Once again, she was faced with the same dilemma: would removal to a hospital environment so terrify him that he would deteriorate still further and far quicker than if she kept him at home?

'He stands a chance with you, Jeanette. I doubt he'll pull through if he comes to us,' was the advice she received. 'He'll resist our handling of him...'

Jasper remained at home where he was attended by their G.P, and nursed by Jeanette. He developed first a chest infection and then an ear infection. Pus now poured from every orifice of his body. Jeanette and Joyce steeled themselves to make a last desperate attempt to save the little boy's life. Other than meticulous nursing, there was nothing more they could do except pray.

Chapter 13

'... *the Mori Poll says 1 in 10 women have
experienced sexual abuse in childhood and more
than a million of today's children will be abused
by the age of 15 ...*'
(*Jean Renvoize,* Incest, a Family Pattern,
Routledge *& Kegan Paul, 1985*)

In the year before Jeanette started her nursing training in the
Mile End Hospital, a baby girl was born. On the day of her
birth, her father deserted his family and was never seen again.

The new baby, Lucy, was to spend the next twenty years of
her life bearing the blame for her unknown father's behaviour.
As soon as she was old enough to understand anything, she
realised that she was different from other children. Her father –
so her mother repeatedly told her – had been a devil, uncaring
and evil. She was the child of that devil and evil blood ran in her
veins. It explained why she was so often naughty; a rebel with a
hot, uncontrolled temper; why she never did anything right. It
also explained why she always felt unloved and unwanted.

It did not altogether explain why her brother, Pip, was
different. Three years older than Lucy, he was a quiet,
withdrawn child and their mother loved him. When Pip was old
enough to go to school, her mother went out to work. Lucy was
looked after by her grandmother and, when she was naughty,
her grandmother locked her in the wardrobe in the bedroom.
Sometimes, even if Lucy had not misbehaved, she would be
locked in the tiny, airless dark prison just to keep her out of
mischief.

Wardrobes were not always prisons. If her mother was in one of her bad moods, punching Lucy with her fists or hitting her with a kitchen utensil, she would crouch in the tiny dark confines of the wardrobe. There she would pretend to be travelling down a long, dark tunnel to an imaginary place where someone loved her. These fantasies helped to lessen her fear of her mother's inexplicable, uncontrolled rages.

When Lucy was five years old, her mother married again and her family moved from Colchester to Norfolk. She now started junior school. Pip's dislike of their new stepfather equalled hers and they drew closer to each other as a result. They now shared a bedroom. Much as Lucy adored Pip, he was of an age to tease. He laughed at her obsessional need to have the curtains drawn so that not even a millimetre of light showed; at her compulsive need to have every ornament and object in their room in an exact position. Somehow, to have things so precisely positioned gave the little girl a sense of security. But Pip would move them, not so much because he wanted them elsewhere but to watch Lucy's inevitable reaction. Losing control, she would scream continuously until her stepfather came in and hit her with his belt, and when he had left she would fly at Pip, taking out her anger and frustration on him. She could not help these outbursts, which seemed to explode from somewhere deep down inside.

More often than not, it was only Lucy who was locked in the potato shed in the garden for punishment. She was very frightened alone in the dark and would stand for hours by the door, waiting for it to open.

With so little joy at home, Lucy was happy to leave the house each morning to go to school. But although she was quick to learn, she did not endear herself to the teachers. She rejected those who showed any interest in her, fearing that they would hate her as much as her mother did once they discovered that she was a devil's child. With her fiery temperament, uncontrolled outbursts of temper and rebelliousness, she was soon designated a trouble maker. Some of the weaker children admired Lucy for her daring and willingness to flout authority; she was a frequent truant.

When Lucy was seven years old, her half-sister was born and was welcomed – as she had never been – by their mother. Lucy and Pip felt even more excluded and had no interest in Maisie, whose arrival they resented. Lucy's behaviour worsened as she grew older and physically stronger. She was often involved in fights with both boys and girls at school; many of them she herself provoked. Like many of her contemporaries she carried a knife, feeling safe from attack with this in her possession.

Lucy, however, could do nothing to protect herself from the horror she was now to endure at the hands of her stepfather. She was eleven years old and had just started at the grammar school when she first woke to find him standing by her bed. Pip had been moved into a room of his own and Maisie now had a cot in Lucy's room. This night, the child was fast asleep as usual. Fear engulfed Lucy as for a split second she thought that at long last the devil had come to claim her. Then she recognised the big, burly man, a menacing figure as he lowered his heavy frame on top of her.

Quickly he forestalled her protests with threats of what he would do if she screamed and brought their mother into the room: he would beat up Pip, as her mother frequently threatened, 'get rid of her' send her away to a place where she might never see Pip again. Lucy was effectively silenced, the fear of what her stepfather would do to her the lesser terror. There was no love in his sexual approaches to her; he satisfied himself without regard for the horror of the ordeal he inflicted. When it was over, Lucy pushed to the back of her mind the pain and fear and felt only the intensity of her relief as her stepfather left the room.

Having lived all her life in the belief that she had inherited bad blood from her father, she was not surprised that her stepfather had chosen her for his victim; she felt in some way she deserved such treatment. It did not occur to her to seek her mother's protection, knowing as she did that it would never be forthcoming. Instead, she accepted that her stepfather had absolute power to repeat the terrible things he had just done, comforting herself with the thought that she still retained some control over the future. So long as she told no one, he would have no reason to beat up Pip or throw him out of the house as he had threatened; or to have her sent away.

He came to her room repeatedly, threatening to kill her if she

128

told anyone. She often wondered if she would die anyway since the weight of his huge frame came perilously close to smothering her. She hated him; she hated her mother for not loving her enough to protect her; she hated herself for being what she was; she hated the life she had had and the life it seemed she was destined to have in the future.

In the years that followed, Lucy often thought as she lay in bed listening for the sound of her stepfather's footsteps, that it would be best for everyone if she could kill herself; but she did not have the courage to end her life. By the time she was thirteen, she was convinced that the badness in her must have grown too, and that before long, everyone in the world would see how evil she really was.

But there were drugs to allay her fears: tranquillisers like monitel and phenobarbitone; purple hearts and amphetamine sulphate or 'speed', anti-depressants such as librium and valium. They could be bought quite cheaply from schoolfriends who knew a girl who worked in a chemist shop and stole what was wanted. When there were no pills, there was always hash to smoke or glue to sniff.

When Lucy was not truanting, she was often causing trouble at school. Once she pulled a knife on one of the female staff who stood too close to her desk when she came over to reprimand her; on another occasion, she attacked a male teacher who happened to touch her. Her emotions were always at flash point.

Once in total despair, she ran away. Within a few days, she was picked up by the police who, suspecting she was in some kind of trouble at home, questioned her closely about her stepfather. She strongly denied he was abusing her, too afraid of his threats of retribution to tell the truth. She was taken home, subjected to her mother's fury and banished once more to the potato shed. Now she was only occasionally allowed back into the house.

In the evenings and at weekends, Lucy worked as an assistant in a butcher's shop and took money from the till. She also went shoplifting, stealing from churches and pickpocketing to raise money for the drugs she needed. She also had a boyfriend – an eighteen-year-old homosexual naval rating. The outward appearance of a conventional boy/girl relationship concealed Lucy's acute aversion to normal sexual advances of the boys she knew.

She was now befriended by the mother of a school friend. The woman approached her on the fields which lay behind the perimeter of the school, where Lucy and some of her friends congregated to take drugs. She invited Lucy back to her home. Her new friend appeared to find no fault with her; on the contrary, she flattered and petted her, gave her little presents and seemed interested in everything Lucy had to say. At thirteen Lucy felt the normal adolescent's craving for affection; and now, somehow, the woman made the transition from verbal affection to a sexual demonstration of caring seem natural.

Lucy did not really enjoy the physical aspects of their association, and was unable to give the deeper, closer affection she knew the woman wanted from her. She mistrusted all emotions, but most of all her own. Was this not just another aspect of the evil within her showing itself in a new guise? Yet her need to be loved drew her back repeatedly to the woman's house. She hoped that her friendship with the young naval rating would squash any rumours of her being what her schoolfriends called 'bent'.

The day came when Lucy was caught thieving. Although she was now fourteen years of age, she still came before the Juvenile Court and was put under a Care Order and allotted a social worker to supervise her behaviour. The social worker's visits to Lucy were routine and achieved nothing since Lucy was an accomplished liar and always reiterated that all was well at school, that she had no problems and was leading an exemplary life. No checks were made on her activities and she continued to steal and take whatever drugs she could obtain. Lucy now tried to ease herself out of her realtionship with the lesbian woman who was making emotional as well as physical demands on her with which Lucy could not cope.

At the end of the year, she left school and, at the same time, left home. She had met a couple called Ken and Laura who seemed to take a genuine interest in her and now offered her a home with them and their three children. It was Lucy's first encounter with what she saw as a loving environment and at first she was happy living there. She found a job at a chicken factory and helped Laura with the children in her free time.

Lucy admired Laura, who was considerably older than her, for her seeming ability to have a good time, particularly with the many men friends who came to the house. Gradually, Laura tried to include her in these sexual orgies. But Lucy's whole being revolted against this contact with the opposite sex. She wanted nothing to do with men who, like her stepfather, demanded the invasion of her body. Moreover, she was beginning to discover that the relationship between Laura and Ken was not the loving, caring one she had supposed. Within a year, Laura walked out on her husband and children. A desperate Ken appealed to Lucy to remain with him and take care of the children, to whom she had become very attached. Unable to leave because she was awaiting her Court appearance for the theft of a car, Lucy stayed on with Ken, paying the price for her continued security by submitting to his sexual demands. She had now progressed from soft to hard drugs which alone seemed to cushion her from the aspects of her life she found so intolerable.

Soon after her eighteenth birthday, Lucy moved into a YWCA hostel. There she met other girls as lonely and in need of affection as herself. She had several casual affairs but her emotions were not seriously involved until she met a girl called Hester. Lucy quickly resumed her former way of life, surviving on hard drugs which, for the most part, dulled any coherent appreciation of what she was doing or the dangers to herself. A friendly homosexual drugs pusher offered them a flat in his house and they moved in.

Lucy had by now adapted to a lesbian relationship, but without regard to the pain she was inflicting she resisted any attempt by Hester to allow the affair to become too emotional. Seeing no hope for the future and hating herself for what she had become, Lucy decided to put an end to her useless existence. She took an overdose of pills. They were insufficient to kill her. Four days later, she was found by a distraught Hester. Lucy once more resumed her old way of life, stealing to feed her addiction to the drugs that alone made life bearable.

Once again Lucy was caught, this time burgling a garage.

131

Soon afterwards, she was caught again, this time in a television shop, and because she was still awaiting trial for the first offence she was sent on remand to prison. Her violent attempt to escape from the courtroom merely aggravated her position; she was assessed as a category 'A' prisoner and given seven days solitary confinement.

Deprived of the drugs to which she was now addicted, with no visitors and no distractions, Lucy fought like a wild animal against her incarceration. Unable to subdue her, the prison authorities ordered the final restraint, known as 'strips'. Lucy was now locked in a bare cell, without even shoes on her feet, and with only a mattress on the bare floor to lie on.

When at last Lucy was returned to her own cell, she was scarcely able to believe her good luck. Hester was there. Apparently, she had gone to pieces after Lucy's rejection of her and had, in a fit of hysterics, smashed the windows of some banks. Inevitably she had been caught in the process and had been remanded to prison. Neither girl could believe their good fortune in being put in the same cell.

Lucy would now happily have remained in prison. But when her case was heard at the Crown Court, she was once again put on probation and found herself back on the streets with no money and no roof over her head. She returned to the flat of the homosexual drug pusher and found herself caught up once more in the self-destructive world of drug addiction.

Lucy was still several months short of twenty when, rejoined now by Hester, they were caught raiding a nearby Chinese restaurant. On this occasion, drugs were found on them and they received a Borstal sentence of six months to two years. Yet again, Hester was allowed to share her cell. Together, the two girls planned and attempted to rob the prison drugs trolley, and were at once separated.

Because of her record of violence, Lucy was not permitted to go to any educational or other communal activities. Alone in her cell, she saw only the prison officers and the prison education officer. On her previous visit to prison, she had learned that it was extremely dangerous to form any kind of close relationship with either the officers or the other female inmates. Many women had formed lesbian relationships, but whilst this could bring privileges, it could also arouse intense jealousies and repercussions if a third person became involved. Lucy resolved to keep well clear of such problems and made it clear to one of the prison officers who approached her that she was not interested in her advances.

She did, however, value the sympathetic interest that one of the staff – a young woman in her thirties – was taking in her. A devout Christian, she gave Lucy religious books to read and spent many hours convincing her that there was a better way of life awaiting her if she would adopt the Christian faith. All her life, Lucy had been unloved, used and abused. She desperately needed to believe there was an alternative to the life she had led for the past twenty years. Her behaviour improved and she was allowed to attend the education classes.

Before the actual date of Lucy's release, she was permitted a week outside the prison. In all the hours she had spent in the older woman's company, it had not once occurred to her that the prison officer was attracted to her, not as a person, but physically. When, during that week she revealed her true feelings for Lucy, Lucy was not only shocked but bitterly disillusioned and wretchedly confused. The revelation of the woman's lesbianism was an exact denial of the Christian teaching she had imparted.

Jeanette now became involved in Lucy's life when she was asked if she could find a place for her to live after her release. Jeanette was desperately short of time.

Little Jasper alone required her full-time attention, quite apart from the twelve other children needing her care and counselling. Moreover, several years previously she had undertaken to edit and produce a monthly magazine for the benefit of the foster parents in the borough. She also had possession of the borough's *Be My Parent* book, which contained details of any child who was difficult to place for fostering or adoption. Jeanette was always available to show the book to any prospective parent of whom a social worker might hear. Calls on her time were made, too, by senior officials who had heard of her remarkable family unit. Councillors, the Director and senior staff, health visitors, even local magistrates, called at her house to meet foster parents and to see at first hand what fostering was really about. Jeanette was also taking in student social workers. She believed that after they had worked for a month in the family circle, they would in the future always see a child primarily as an individual and only secondarily as a case history.

Nevertheless, as a Christian Jeanette wanted to help this young prisoner if she could and, as it so happened, one of the children's health visitors with whom Jeanette had become friendly was able to offer Lucy a temporary room in her flat. But for the persistent attentions of the prison officer, Lucy might have settled down. However, the woman had no intention of letting Lucy go. Playing on the girl's loneliness and her increasing lack of self-confidence, she persuaded her to continue the relationship for which Lucy herself had little enthusiasm. It went against every concept of the Christian teaching that she had wanted to embrace.

Lucy longed to confide in Jeanette, but her unwelcome lover warned her in the strongest terms against such confidences. Only this past week, she stressed, Jeanette had caused a furore by revealing that the local minister who was teaching some of her children was a homosexual and that she was not prepared to accept him as a spiritual leader. If Jeanette were to learn of Lucy's lesbian associations, the older woman warned, she would have nothing more to do with her. Lucy moved into her own tiny flat in Upper North Street. She was no longer taking drugs and had no real friend to turn to for advice. Her despair deepened. For several months, she was too lethargic to make the effort to go out and buy food. Slowly she was starving herself to death. Jeanette, who saw her from time to time, noticed the girl's loss of weight, but she was unaware of the true reasons for it, since Lucy was inarticulate in her presence.

Lucy's weight had reduced to five stone when she was finally rushed into intensive care in the nearby hospital. For several days, she hovered between life and death. Learning of this new tragedy, Jeanette realised for the first time how desperate the girl must have been, and she determined to find out the cause. Lucy might be twenty-two years old but, judging by her past record, she was as much in need of a family and mother to support her as any child.

As soon as Lucy had returned to her flat some six weeks later Jeanette sent her a message worded with customary bluntness.

'You'd best come round and see me some time in the next seven days or I'll want to know the reason why.'

Too weak to prevent the tears she had vowed as a small child never to shed again, Lucy clung to the hastily scribbled note knowing that she had been offered a lifeline, yet at the same time feeling terrified that Jeanette would discover that she wasn't after all worth helping – that no one could ever help her because she was the devil's child.

Chapter 14

'23% of neglected children, 32% of the emotionally abused children and 39% of the physically injured children were living with their natural parents. A quarter of the registered children were living with their natural mother alone, and another quarter with her and a father substitute.
(Initial Findings, 1985, from NSPCC Register Research)

Jeanette made no attempt to force Lucy's confidences. The experiences of her own childhood gave her an instinctive understanding of the inarticulateness which locked in a girl like Lucy, whose self-evaluation was non-existent. She encouraged her to spend her weekends with the Family and was satisfied for the moment gradually to win Lucy's trust.

At first, Lucy was convinced that there must be some hidden drawback to the happy, caring family circle which Jeanette had created. Not only did Jeanette seem to care deeply for every single child and for each one to respond as if she were their real mother, but all the children seemed to care for and protect one another. They were even prepared to accept the appalling stench in the sitting-room caused by Jasper, the tiny five-year-old West Indian boy. Miraculously, he had survived the infections which had so nearly caused his death. Since then, still sickly and terrified of any attempt to handle him, the child had spent the last six months crouching like a wild animal between his bed on the settee and a nearby armchair. He was still incontinent and the atmosphere in the room was almost intolerable even though it had been refurbished when recently, the effects of a serious ear infection had necessitated his admittance to hospital despite the difficulties of treating him in that alien environment. Jeanette was still the only person who could handle the boy. She had at last overcome his paranoid fear of water by taking him into the bath with her, often being badly bitten in the process. Now that his fear had lessened, she put Wendy in the bath with him.

One evening a chance phone call necessitated her leaving the two young children alone in the bathroom together. When she returned she saw that somehow Wendy had succeeded in getting Jasper out of the water and was doing her best to dry the struggling child.

'Don't you hit me or I'll hit yer back,' the little girl was saying. 'And don't bite me neither 'cos I'll bite you. Now lift up your arm, and turn round so's I can dry your back!'

Wendy proceeded to dress him.

Despite the frequent chest infections from which she still suffered, Wendy had grown into a bright, intelligent six-year-old. She was enjoying school and hated it when ill-health obliged her to miss classes. Her inclination to mother Jasper was a godsend since from that time on, Jeanette ceased to be the only person who could cope with the still half-wild little boy. Jasper was now in a cot upstairs, which he used as a rabbit might use a burrow, and the children, including Sylvie, helped with the attempts to teach him to climb the stairs. But nearly always he had to be carried. His physical condition was slowly improving, but he was still very undersized for his age and his mental age was indistinguishable from that of a baby.

That winter, it was bitterly cold and there was a heavy snowfall. Jasper screamed with terror at the strange white world around him. The children brought handfuls of snow indoors until gradually he became accustomed to it.

However, it was a student social worker, a six-foot-tall West Indian, who was first able to persuade the child to go out for a walk in the snow with him. Joyce, returning one day from work, was touched by the sight of the gangly young man walking hand in hand with the diminutive Jasper, whilst he chattered reassuringly to him in a soft, accented voice. Although the little boy showed no sign as yet of being able to talk, his animal screech was heard far less often.

Sylvie had now left school and was doing everything within her limits to help around the house, but she was still unhappily awre of those limits. As her eighteenth birthday drew near, Jeanette discussed a coming-of-age birthday party with her, but Sylvie explained carefully that she did not really feel old enough to be a grown-up and would prefer to wait until she was twenty-one, by which time she might have become like the other girls. She still worried a great deal about her 'difference' and she was happiest in the company of seven-year-old Sandra. That Sandra was the more responsible of the two was never remarked upon.

Jeanette had other matters beside the children to concern her. Eighteen months after the death of her stepfather, her mother had had a stroke and been taken to Lewisham hospital where Jeanette visited her as often as possible. But she never made a full recovery and at Easter, her mother died. Robbie, who had never lost his affection for the woman who had taken him into her home in Bromley and who had tried to help him learn to read, obtained leave from the army and went with Jeanette to the funeral.

It was impossible for Jeanette to feel sad, convinced as she was that her mother had blamed her for the break-up of the family. It was she knew, the typical reaction of a parent caught up in the trauma of incest, finding it easier to think of her child as the perpetrator of the trouble rather than the victim. Jeanette had long since ceased to expect affection from her or even recognition of her accomplishments.

Yet Jeanette herself did not deny that her mother had had many good points. She had always been a willing granny to the children – Jeanette's, her grandchildren, or those in the neighbourhood in need of care or comfort. She had been much liked by her neighbours. But understandably, Jeanette felt no personal sense of loss at her passing.

In June, Catrina's adoption was finalised and the whole family celebrated with a party. Adoption was something the girl had been so impatient to achieve that she herself had applied for the papers and had persuaded Jeanette to complete them! But Jeanette was far from happy about the seventeen-year-old girl.

She was always well-behaved but Jeanette was concerned none the less. Catrina seemed to have valid reasons why she had not, as her teachers expected, passed her exams. Jeanette discovered that she had been playing truant and had skilfully covered her absences. She refused to explain her behaviour.

The girl was petite, dark-eyed and attractive and obviously interested in boys. She had developed a relationship with a younger boy who often visited the house. Jeanette now gave far more responsibility to Lucy, feeling she could no longer rely on Catrina to give her full attention to the little ones in her absence. She resolved to keep a close eye on the girl, more especially as she would be leaving home after her eighteenth birthday in October.

In the meantime, she knew Catrina would be out of harm's way during the summer holidays down at the farmhouse in Sussex. Farleys had now become the family's regular retreat where they went whenever the holidays permitted their exodus from London. The children loved the country life and the freedom it allowed them.

This summer Lucy went with them. The six-week holiday with the family had a profound effect upon the girl. For the first time in her life, Lucy was aware of a feeling of total security. Jeanette did what she could to restore her trust in the Christian way of life and to convince her of her value as a human being. She spent many long hours counselling Lucy, most of their talks of necessity taking place at night since there was scant opportunity for any privacy during the long summer days. They would take the car, which provided a natural confessional box, down to the edge of the sea or along a quiet lane and there Lucy talked of her horrific past experiences and her fears for the future. Sometimes her need to confide would continue for three or four hours, but Jeanette was always willing to forgo sleep, having long since forgotten what it meant to have an undisturbed night.

Nobody wanted to return to London at the end of that summer holiday. The second of the two houses in Campbell Road had still not been renovated and by now the first was beginning to look dilapidated. It was over three years since they had first arranged to move there and the family pattern had changed during that long period. Some of the older children had left home; new children had arrived; Sylvie, who had once longed for a room all to herself, was anxious to share with another girl. Without exception, the entire family would greatly have preferred to abandon all thoughts of a move to Campbell Road and to live permanently in the country had such a thing been possible.

The children settled down once more at their various schools, with the exception of Ellen. Now eleven years old, she had moved to the secondary school which her sister, Margaret, had attended. At the age of fifteen, Margaret was following in her mother's footsteps and already prostituting herself, a fact known to the older boys at the school. Ellen bore a remarkable family likeness to Margaret and in consequence she was often taunted by the older boys, who would ask her 'How much do you charge?' Something, Jeanette realised, must be done to protect Ellen, and she set about the problem of trying to change her school.

Jeanette now received a phone call from the Parents for Children agency, who urgently required her help.

'We want a bridging parent for a twelve-year-old girl who needs to be assessed for her suitability for fostering,' Jeanette was informed. The girl had been in two Children's Homes since her previous fostering had broken down and was considered so violent and disruptive that neither would keep her.

Clare had first been taken into care at the age of eleven weeks. Her mother, a seventeen-year-old prostitute, had attempted to keep her baby after the child's birth, but had finally abandoned her with a blanket and a bottle in the night-club where she worked. The baby was put in a residential nursery where she grew into a happy, smiling five-year-old with her Greek Cypriot father's large brown eyes and olive skin. Her mother, whose earlier visits had ceased for the past two years, suddenly arrived on the scene again. The little girl became unsettled, unable as she was to understand why her mother could not keep her or why she had no father. Plans were made to have her fostered.

The foster parents chosen for Clare were welcoming and at first could find no fault with the child. They had, in fact, wanted to foster a boy as company for their young son Giles, but compromised by cutting Clare's hair short, dressing her in boy's clothes and allowing her to play only with toys like Action Man. Moderately affluent, with a large house and garden, they sent Clare to the private boys' prep school which Giles attended. There were no other girls. There she was permitted to wear a girl's uniform skirt, but the moment she returned home, she was ordered to change back into boys' trousers. When she was given a doll, her foster mother confiscated it.

Clare's foster father was an easy-going man who did not appear to mind what she did, but her relationship with her foster mother slowly deteriorated. Clare began to lie and steal, both at school and at home. Her social worker seemed unable to understand how deeply the child was affected by her foster mother's determination to bring her up as a boy. She frequently ran away, but made no mention to her social worker of her growing fear and dislike of her foster mother.

She was no longer allowed to eat with the family but had her meals on her own. When she was naughty or defiant, her foster mother threatened to throw her out of the window. She frequently beat Clare with a wooden spoon or cane on her hands and on the soles of her feet. One day, in exasperation, she plunged the child's arm into boiling water and threatened Clare with severe retribution if she did not tell the casualty officer at the hospital that she had been sliding in the kitchen in her socks and that the scald had been an accident.

Matters came to a head when Clare's foster mother decided she had had enough trouble with the child and demanded that Clare be removed immediately. Her social worker arranged for her to be put in a Children's Home in West London. Clare had spent five years in a middle class environment and it was far from easy for her to adapt to the lifestyle of the Home. The other children made fun of her accent and manners, recognising at once that she was different from themselves and at first deliberately ostracised her. Disruptive and naughty, she would be verbally reprimanded for her bad behaviour but not punished. The lack of any firm adult control compounded her own fears that she could not control herself and she became more daring, telling the teachers to 'fuck off' and even on

141

occasions brandishing a knife. Still she was not punished. Gradually, the other children formed a gang of which Clare became the leader. At first, they only roamed the streets scaring old people and shopkeepers; but then some of the other children started mugging old ladies. They stole a car and deliberately crashed it. They had their own secret meeting place where they could hide from the law and there were meetings with friendly, rival gangs from a few miles away.

Clare's influence upon the other children in the Home was now only too apparent. She was removed and sent to a similar Home a short distance away. By now she was twelve and a half. She was frequently in the company of older children who were drinking, taking drugs, sniffing glue, and totally out of adult control. Looked up to by the other children in her gang as their leader, it was vital for her to appear tough. She adopted a skinhead haircut and now, of her own accord, wore boys clothes – track suit trousers and an old, long black crombie style jacket. She had long since lost any desire to appear feminine. A last vain attempt was made by her social worker to send her to a new foster home. Clare refused to go and the Home advised the Social Services Department that they could not cope with her.

Jeanette's first introduction to Clare was when a young social worker called Louise drove the girl to Mornington Grove. Louise climbed out of the car, her face white with anxiety as Jeanette came out of the house to greet them.

'Clare broke the gear lever in my car and I had to borrow this one to get her here! Now she says she won't get out,' she said, adding resignedly, 'and she's threatening to kill everyone!'

Jeanette told her to go and make herself a cup of coffee whilst she dealt with the situation. She opened the car door and introduced herself.

'Fuck off!' was Clare's reply.

'Out!' said Jeanette, surveying the young skinhead in her extraordinary outfit with interest. 'Or do I have to lift you out?'

'I ain't fucking moving.'

'And I'm not asking, I'm telling you – *get out of the car!*'

Jeanette's voice gave no inkling of her private misgivings. Clare was no little girl who could be lifted physically out of the vehicle and carried into the house against her will. Jeanette was

142

far from certain what she would do if the girl stayed where she was. She was convinced of one thing – that no child must ever be allowed to believe that he or she was in control of the situation – and least of all a child like Clare who had been accustomed to terrorising adults and children alike!

But the note of authority in Jeanette's voice had been enough to convince Clare – as it had so many other children before her – that for the time being anyway, she would do best to comply with the order. After the briefest of pauses, she said:

'Okay, keep yer cool. I'm coming! But I ain't staying long!'

'Like a cup of coffee?' Jeanette asked in a normal voice.

'Fuck off and leave me alone!' was the reply.

Jeanette already knew of Clare's reputation for violence and had instructed the children to remain downstairs whilst she tried to reassure Clare that she would soon settle in. Clare announced firmly that she had no intention of doing so. Moreover, she'd do just as she pleased.

'You're going to do exactly what you are told,' Jeanette informed her quietly. 'Your days of telling everyone else what to do are over. Now are you coming downstairs to lunch?'

'Fuck off!' was Clare's now familiar reply.

But she did come down, banging everything within reach before she sat down noisily at the long table. Someone put a plate of food in front of her. Deliberately she spilled the contents.

'I don't eat no dinner,' she said, putting her elbows on the table and her chin in her hands.

'Don't you come that with me,' Jeanette said, 'because I'm not frightened of you. Any more nonsense and I'll pick you up and march you upstairs quicker than you'd believe.'

'I gotta gang. I'll tell 'em to get you. They gotta knife. They'll fucking get your guts! I gotta big black man what'll slice you up!'

Jeanette drew a long exaggerated sigh and shrugged her shoulders.

'Oh, no! Can you believe it, we've got another one!' she said as if the Family encountered young braggarts like Clare every day. The children at once took up the chorus: 'Not another one!'

Only Clare's dark, liquid brown eyes betrayed her confusion.

143

Her face expressed a continuing defiance but she realised that somehow Jeanette had defused her challenge. Slowly, very slowly, she began to eat her lunch.

Jeanette regarded that drooped childish head, her short moment of triumph swept aside by a great wave of pity. There was a sad vulnerability about that outrageous skinhead haircut beneath which, she knew very well, there was just another lost, frightened child.

Chapter 15

*'Once in a while both parents are involved in
group sex with their children... i.e. where a
mother and father lead their children through
ever-increasing orgiastic adventures...'*
(Summit & Kryso. Multiple Sex, *quoted in Jean
Renvoize,* Incest, a Family Pattern, *Routledge
& Kegan Paul, 1985)*

Catrina and Lucy had become friendly, and Jeanette arranged
for the two girls to share a flat since one had become vacant next
door to the house in Mornington Grove. There, Jeanette felt,
she could keep an eye on both of them. Now eighteen, Catrina
had left school, but was still giving Jeanette cause for concern.

Peter Stickings, the headmaster of Bow School for Boys, an
excellent local state school, had given Catrina a job as a
secretarial assistant. He took a special interest in those of
Jeanette's boys who attended the school and he had become a
family friend. On the surface all seemed to be well, but Catrina
was still reticent about her private life. Whilst the family were
in Sussex that summer, she had disappeared for a short time.

Jeanette now learned from Peter Stickings that the girl was
head over heels in love with the brother of one of the teachers at
the school and was living with him. The relationship was a
deeply unhappy one. For the young man it was a casual affair of
which he had soon tired, but Catrina could not bring herself to
acknowledge the fact.

Jeanette made no attempt to interfere since Catrina showed
no inclination to confide in her. Although she continued to

worry about her, she felt Catrina must learn to cope with her emotions like any other adolescent. When Catrina visited the Family, which she always did unaccompanied by her boyfriend, Jeanette simply reminded her that she was always there if Catrina was in need of her help. Catrina threatened suicide whenever the young man attempted to break with her, but although this failed to alter his attitude, she still would not admit that the affair was over.

Fortunately, Jeanette had no need to worry about her other eighteen-year-old, Mick. He had grown into a strong, lovable young man with a surprisingly gentle side to his nature, and was intensely loyal to the Family. He had moved into a flat of his own, but visited them often. Physically tough, he had no difficulty in obtaining work and was self-supporting. Quite often, he brought presents for the younger children, and remained in frequent touch with those of his 'brothers' and 'sisters' who, like himself, had left home.

Nor indeed was she worried about Tom who was now employed by the Social Services in West London as a Domiciliary Care Attendant. He seemed well suited to his job. He was perfectly content caring for old people in their homes and Jeanette knew she had no need to worry about his future. Nor, indeed, was she worried about Catrina's brother, Simon, who was away at college studying for a social sciences degree.

Clare, meanwhile, was determined from the moment she walked into the house not to relinquish her rôle as the gang boss without a fight. For once, Jeanette reversed her policy of trying to make a child feel welcomed and wanted. She believed that Clare needed from the start to understand that she was now in a place where like it or not she must conform; that her threats to run away, to report Jeanette to the social worker, were pointless.

As the days and weeks passed, she realised that Clare was an intelligent child whose behaviour could be very deceptive. At times, she resorted to the violent temper tantrums of a toddler; at others, to the abusive bullying of the erstwhile gang leader. She could lie, cheat and steal whilst maintaining an appearance of complete innocence. She went out of her way to test Jeanette's insistence that she cared for and about her. On one occasion she upturned rack after rack of shoes on display in a shop, acting so fast that the floor was littered with them before Jeanette managed to grab hold of her.

Anyone but Jeanette might have been furiously angry, but her sense of humour prevailed.

'Don't worry!' she told the shocked assistant. 'She won't hurt you and she'll put them all back before we leave.'

Underlying her humour was her long-held understanding of the need of children like hers constantly to test the degree of her caring. It was natural for them to believe themselves worthless and unlovable, and since they had never before come upon someone who did care about their happiness and safety, they were mistrustful of her. They needed to know that even their extremes of bad behaviour would not result in her rejection of them.

It was not long before Clare realised that the other children, who had been cautioned by Jeanette, were not reacting either to her tempers or to her threats of physical violence. She began to relax and if no one seemed to be looking at her, could even be seen playing with Wendy's dolls.

Eventually, Clare was unable to resist playing 'Mums and Dads' with Sandra and Ellen. Although she refused to relinquish her boy's hair cut, she spent a great deal of time washing and brushing it; she wore dresses, used scent and blushed whenever someone paid her a compliment. She also began to show an interest in learning to cook, sew and knit.

By the January of the following year, Clare had settled down so well that Jeanette agreed with her social worker that she should remain with the Family permanently. Clare was thrilled. Nevertheless, Jeanette knew that there was still a long way to go before the girl could emerge from the confusions of her childhood experiences and find her true identity. In common with many emotionally damaged children, she had a curious need to hurt herself. She would often give herself superficial cuts, tip hot coffee over herself, bang into things. There were times when her hatred of herself extended to other people and she would do or say something to hurt them. It was a facet of Clare's character Jeanette knew she must help her to overcome.

Catrina's adoption had put the idea into the heads of all the children that they, too, could legally become members of the Roberts Family. But much as Jeanette herself would have liked to adopt every single child, her financial situation made this impossible. An adopted child received no fostering allowance at this time,* and she was entirely dependent upon her children's allowances and Joyce's salary to maintain her huge family. Nevertheless, she had applied to adopt three of her teenagers, Tom, Jason and Natalie.

Tom had not seen his father since he was two years old, but now, unexpectedly, the man opposed the adoption on the grounds that his woman had left him, and, he said, 'Tom can look after the kids while I go out to work!' This reply was all the Judge needed to grant Jeanette's application, and Tom's adoption was finalised, a week after Jason's and Natalie's.

Jeanette now had five adopted children and twelve foster children preparing for their annual summer holiday at the farmhouse. A week before the end of the summer term, she was approached by one of the London borough adoption agencies. One of their field workers wanted to discuss the future of three highly disturbed brothers who had been sexually molested by their parents. They were 'In Care' and living in a Children's Home in South London. The agency was hoping that Jeanette could foster two of the three boys.

Jeanette immediately reiterated her long-standing principle that it was wrong to separate natural brothers and sisters. If she were to take the boys, she said, it would be all three or none at all. She went to the Home to meet them. The eldest boy, Ted – a dark, good looking teenager of fifteen – was uncommunicative and it was the youngest of the brothers, Roger, who showed her round the Home. Jeanette was shocked to discover that all the doors were kept locked because the children stole or broke each other's possessions. It was a state of affairs indicative of an undisciplined environment which she felt was quite unsuitable for young children such as this little boy.

*This has now changed. The 1975 Children's Act (effective for a seven-year experimental period 1982-1989) permits local authorities to pay the Approved Adoption Allowance when a child is placed for adoption and after legal adoption until the child is 18. This is tailored to the needs of each family.

Her first impression of Roger was of a sad, confused child and it soon became clear to Jeanette that he was very uncertain whether or not he wanted to be fostered, although he looked momentarily happier when she told him she wanted to foster his older brothers, Ted and Brian, too.

Communication with the middle brother, Brian, was even more impossible. The boy was clearly unable to understand the implications of being fostered. The Social Services had implied that he was a spastic and brain damaged and could do nothing for himself. His brothers did everything for him, cut up his food, made his bed, cleaned him – a continual necessity since he was frequently incontinent. He was certainly not a pre-possessing sight. He had a noticeable squint, his eyes looking in opposite directions as he stared up at Jeanette. His front teeth protruded and one, which had supposedly been broken, had a horrible looking silver cap which increased the oddity of his appearance. She was told by the other children that there was no point her trying to talk to him because he was 'daft'.

Jeanette learned that he went to a special school in the area for the mentally handicapped and decided to visit it. She was impressed by the atmosphere of the school and was told by the headmaster that Brian had made remarkable progress since he had arrived there six years ago. They had even improved his personal habits which were supposedly due to his parents deviant training. He masturbated frequently and publicly and made sexual approaches to the other children and staff.

Jeanette also visited Roger's school where she learned that he was two years behind with his work, was violent, hit the other children and was prone to furious temper tantrums. He was so disruptive that despite their sympathetic approach to the boy's problems, they felt they could no longer keep him there.

Jeanette well understood why the Social Services were so anxious to find an alternative to the Children's Home for these three boys. She had been very deeply shocked when they informed her that the sexual abuse by their parents had continued to take place within the very Children's Home which had been selected for their protection. This outrageous state of affairs had only recently come to light. It was now known to have been happening over a period of six months but, unbelievably, no one had discovered it until, quite by chance, a member of staff had noticed the locked door of the visitor's room. When Jeanette agreed to foster the boys, she knew only these bare details from their Social Service records.

Over the next few years, however, she was to piece together from their recollections the shocking reality of their horrific childhood. Ted was the eldest of the three brothers. His ordeal had begun when he was about four. He remembered frequent beatings by his parents, sometimes with a buckled belt. He remembered being beaten if he did not pay attention when his mother or father showed him pictures of naked men and women together in a bed. He hated looking at the pictures, but hated it still more when he was obliged to stand in the bedroom and watch his parents in bed together. At that age, he had little or no understanding of sex and although he was uncomfortable watching them or looking at the strange pictures, he assumed that all parents took such special interest in their anatomy and included their children in their sexual activities.

When he grew older, he started school. There were many days when his mother kept him back from his lessons because she wanted him to touch her, fondle her or because she wanted to touch him. He wished very much that she would leave him alone but if he showed any sign of rebelling, he was severely beaten. When his brother Brian was born, he too was beaten as soon as he was old enough to be naughty. Ted had understood vaguely from his parents that his brother was mentally backward and although Ted was only five, he was frequently called upon to take care of the toddler.

Once, when Brian had been trying to eat a tube of glue left by his father on a table within his reach, his mother had snatched it away and thrown it on to the fire in one of her sudden tempers. The glue flared up and spat its burning contents over Brian's legs. As a consequence, he was still terribly scarred despite skin grafts.

When the youngest brother, Roger, was born, their mother seemed even less able to cope and the beatings became more frequent. The occasions in the bedroom or sitting-room when Ted and Brian were obliged to watch their parents having sex continued. Now they were often made to strip off their clothes

150

and join in, their presence seeming to excite their parents to greater excesses. Ted dreaded these orgies. Brian did not seem so disturbed by them and often played with his own body even when his parents were absent. It embarrassed Ted to see the little boy behaving in this way. Now he was at school, he was aware from the behaviour of other children that this was not the normal thing to do and that certain parts of the body were considered private; but he still had no way of knowing whether the parents of the other schoolchildren behaved any differently in the privacy of their homes from his own mother and father. He assumed that they did. He wondered sometimes if the other boys disliked it as much as he did and wished his parents would leave them alone.

By the time he was nearly eight, Ted's mother had become more violent in her treatment of the children. Her temper flared quickly and was uncontrolled, often unprovoked. Ted was on the receiving end of one such outburst when she suddenly picked up one of his metal cars and aimed it at his head. He was so badly cut he had to be taken to the hospital where a non-accidental injury was immediately suspected since the bruises on his body from the frequent beatings were a further indication that he was the victim of parental violence. He was kept in hospital and the Social Services were called. They arranged for him to be sent directly to a Children's Home where, they told him, he would be much happier than he was at home.

At the age of seven, Ted was upset by this enforced separation from his brothers, particularly from little Roger to whom he was protectively attached. He thought he was only going to the Home for a holiday. Although Ted was now free from the constant beatings by his parents from Monday to Friday, he was allowed to spend the weekends at home. The beatings and the sexual involvement began again. He told no one and the weekend activities remained undiscovered.

Ted's reappearance at home had thrown his two-year-old brother, Roger, into deep confusion. The little boy had been told by his mother when Ted went into the Children's Home that his brother had been naughty and, as a result, had been turned into a stick – a walking stick – which was then put in Roger's bedroom as a warning to him. He never doubted that

151

this stick was Ted and began to have terrible nightmares in which he, too, was being turned into a stick as his mother threatened. When his brother reappeared in person, he could not understand why there were two Teds, nor why Ted went away again when it was time for him to be returned to the Children's Home. Roger's stutter became more pronounced.

Their parents' physical abuse of Ted had alerted the Social Services to the risks to the younger boys. Although they were unaware of the sexual abuse, it was noticed that both Brian and Roger were being beaten; that the house was dirty and the mother, who was still only in her early twenties, was clearly unable to manage. The two boys were taken into Care and sent to join Ted at the Children's Home. Visiting rights were permitted to the parents, who were told they could take the three children out for the day once a week, possibly to the park and for a meal in a Wimpy Bar.

They did neither, taking the boys home to continue their sexual perversions, now insisting that the older ones should do whatever their mother demanded to give her pleasure. Only Brian, whose emotional retardation protected him totally, appeared to enjoy these sordid sessions. Any disinclination on the boys' part to do what was demanded of them invoked a beating.

Eventually it was noticed by a member of staff at the Children's Home that the boys often returned from these parental outings severely bruised and, since they had not in fact had tea at the Wimpy Bar as was supposed, obviously hungry. The fact that they were being taken back to their home came to light. The matter was referred back to the Courts, as always a lengthy procedure. It was finally ordered that the boys' parents should visit them only once a month and on the premises of the Home – and then under strict supervision.

This supervision order was never enforced. The family were given the use of one of the playrooms and left undisturbed. Their father would put a chair under the door handle to prevent them from being interrupted. Out came the pornographic books and pictures, and the sexual activities continued as they had at home.

Although the parents brought sweets and cakes for the boys,

they never returned home empty-handed. There was an unlocked cupboard in the room containing food which they stole without compunction. Sometimes their mother showed the boys photographs of two dead babies – one stillborn and one she had miscarried. She forced the boys to look at the photographs, telling them that it was their fault the babies had died; their fault because the babies' deaths had been the result of the distress they had caused her by being sent to the Children's Home.

The boys were too frightened of the threats of the beatings they would receive if they told anyone what happened during these visits ever to talk about it. The visits continued month after month, before finally the truth came to light. The parents were violently opposed to the subsequent plan to have the boys fostered since there would be no further opportunity to continue their sexual exploitation of their children, and they now surreptitiously tried to persuade the boys to object to the concept of fostering.

They threatened that they would kill their sons rather than see them fostered; told them that it was their duty to burn down the foster parents' house so that they could not live in it; and that as a last resort they would be better off dead and should throw themselves under a bus or train rather than remain there. All three boys had taken these adult warnings seriously. Roger once tried to put an end to his mental conflict by running in front of a car. Fortunately, the driver managed to avoid him and he was not killed or even injured.

Astonishingly, their house mother also had told them that they would hate being in an ordinary home, because they would have no toys or games to play with. Jeanette never discovered whether the woman could possibly have been influenced by the boys' parents. But she was unaware of these details when the three boys joined the Family, who were busily preparing for the summer holiday exodus to the farm in Sussex.

It was whilst these preparations were taking place that Jeanette received a phone call from her old friend Ken Start of the Springboard Housing Association. He had been contacted by a social worker known to Jeanette, Diana, who had considerable problems concerning an eighteen-year-old girl and her two brothers. Their mother had recently died and he had been asked by Diana if he could find accommodation for the children, since their stepfather had refused to take responsibility for them. But he was uneasy about the situation. The girl, Alison, he explained, was anxious to keep the little family together, but her youngest brother, Ben, had muscular dystrophy and her sixteen-year-old brother, Neal, was a Down's Syndrome child. He felt they would need support if he were to provide a flat for them to live in.

But there were further problems. Ben's health was steadily deteriorating and it was thought that he would soon be relegated to a wheelchair. He had been truant from school for the past two years and had been the subject of physical abuse from his stepfather.

Neal, however, had been the centre of his mother's – and stepfather's – attention; her's had been protective and concerned for his future, his stepfather's had been for his own popularity. It had been his habit to take his son every evening to the pub where Neal was plied with drinks. The boy's subsequent clownish behaviour had become the evening entertainment for the locals. Used to his mother's affection and the adulation he had received at the pub, Neal was feeling very deeply his mother's sudden disappearance, which to him was inexplicable since his understanding of death was limited to that of an inarticulate eight-year-old. Clearly Alison was going to find it very difficult to cope.

Jeanette at once agreed to meet Diana to discuss the possibility of the three children moving into the flat below Lucy's, which, fortuitously, happened to be vacant. She left the meeting, having agreed on impulse to foster both Neal and Ben. They were to join the Family in Sussex as soon as it could be arranged by the Social Services Department. Their sister, Alison, would be given the flat below Lucy's and be freed from her self-imposed burden.

There was an additional factor motivating Jeanette to foster Neal. During the past years, she had grown very attached to Sylvie, learning from her how especially difficult life could be for the mentally handicapped. Perhaps, Jeanette thought, she could also improve the quality of life for the Down's Syndrome

154

child, Neal, whose status had been reduced to that of a buffoon. Was it possible that Sylvie had been sent to her so that she could learn how to help these most needy of all children? So that her existing children could learn to be tolerant with the mentally handicapped? She was convinced her impulsive decision was the right one.

There were, therefore, fifteen children enjoying the countryside. The atmosphere was, as always when they were at Farleys, relaxed and happy, and Jeanette expressed to Joyce her growing conviction that they should remove permanently to the country.

'It wouldn't work,' Joyce argued. 'Where would we ever find schools for the children miles away from a city? Besides, they are city kids and their birth families all live in London. Parental visiting would be difficult...'

Jeanette thought that would be no bad thing. Officialdom chose to make an issue of what was called a bond – a blood tie that supposedly existed between parents and their natural children. But all too frequently, no such bond did exist to be broken by a child's removal from parental contact.

Ironically, they now learned that the Campbell Road property was ready for their occupation. It was four long years since Jeanette and Joyce had first talked with such eagerness of having the extra space afforded by the two combined houses. But after such a lapse of time, the prospect had lost its desirability. Moreover, there had been seven new additions to the family in the interim and although it would be a godsend to leave the hopelessly cramped quarters at Mornington Grove, there was not going to be any space to spare in Campbell Road.

Nevertheless, plans for the removal were put in hand. The older members of the family, Jason, Lucy and Ted, undertook the bulk of the heavy work, giving up their holiday weekends to travel to London for the purpose. Lucy was now almost part of the Family and had taken on much of the domestic work as well as the care of the younger children. Although she avoided communication with any adult other than Jeanette, she would converse with the little ones. She was a capable and practical girl and now that she was physically strong again, her help in making Campbell Road habitable for the Family was immense.

But, even as they moved into their new home, secretly

Jeanette was nursing the idea that they would not remain there for long. She dreamed of a magical offering of a big house in the country, surrounded by fields and garden, where there would be room for the pets the children wanted; where they could, in the gentler, slower-paced atmosphere, more easily come to terms with the physical and emotional damage inflicted on them in the past.

Jeanette's faith had not weakened but grown stronger with the years. Now she did what she had always done when she needed help – she prayed.

Chapter 16

'90% of Rapists, 30% of Rape Victims, 40% of
Alcoholics and Drug Addicts, 75% of Prostitutes, 30% of Children in Care and almost all
Male Prostitutes were abused children.' These
figures are related as an average of all surveys
undertaken worldwide during the last 15 years.
(Incest Crisis Line, Information Sheet, 1987)

It was inconceivable to those who had not met Jeanette Roberts
that she could foster so many emotionally disturbed children
whilst maintaining a real family atmosphere. Many supposed
that she must run her establishment much on the lines of a
Children's Home and that they must accordingly lack the close
ties and relationships existing in ordinary families.

Those who visited Jeanette's home were at first astonished
and then obliged to change their preconceived ideas. To her
foster children, Jeanette was far more than a foster mother – she
was their Mum, loved, trusted, respected and a fierce champion
of their rights. She encouraged them to respect each other and to
consider every other child under her roof as a brother or sister.
Each was told of the other's problems and was expected to
contribute understanding, sympathy, support and companionship. Rivalries and sibling jealousies were never allowed to
become physically violent.

Jeanette's practice – begun when she had first started
fostering – of holding family conferences to make democratic
decisions for the Family had proved its value. Each child felt
directly involved in the welfare of them all. But paramount in

157

the extraordinary unity of the Family was the spirit of mutual caring which emanated from Jeanette herself. No child was ever denied access to her regardless of when they might need it. Whether it was one of the youngsters waking terrified from a nightmare, with whom she must sit and give comfort, or whether it was an older child who needed to talk about past experiences and anxieties, Jeanette was always available.

In part, the very size of Jeanette's family helped her to achieve this degree of mothering. She was a strict disciplinarian and each child capable of it knew that they must clean and tidy their own room. The older ones took it in turns, on a rota system, to prepare meals, cook, wash up, shop, do the washing and ironing, and care for the younger ones. Sometimes, when the children first arrived, they would rebel against these domestic chores but they quickly adapted to this discipline, especially when it was explained to them that Jeanette could not give them the help and counselling they needed if they did not all assist her in this way.

During that summer holiday prior to the move to Campbell Road, the Family were all aware that Jeanette's time would have many calls upon it with the five newly arrived boys. She was particularly concerned about Neal, the Down's Syndrome boy, who, from the time of his arrival at the farmhouse with his brother Ben, was aggressive and violent towards the other children. When he was not shouting abuse or attacking one of them in a fit of temper, he was shouting for a Guinness. It was several days before Joyce, whose bedroom adjoined his, went to his room to find him in considerable physical distress. She realised that he was suffering from withdrawal symptoms because he was now deprived of the large quantities of alcohol he had been drinking regularly at his stepfather's pub.

Although violent towards everyone else, he was not so towards Jeanette and obeyed her immediately, treating her, she soon realised, as he must have treated his mother. She discovered that he had not understood that his mother had died, and she now told him the facts and tried to comfort him as best she could. He was very distressed.

The only other person he related to was his brother Ben, towards whom he was fiercely protective. Ben quickly made friends with the other boys and there was a touching example of Neal's desire to protect his brother when he attacked one of Ben's friends who was indulging in some harmless horseplay. When Neal raced to his brother's defence, Jeanette had to get two of the bigger boys to restrain him and explain that Ben was only playing and had been in no danger.

Shortly after they had settled down in the new house, Jeanette set about finding a suitable school for Ben. He had been allocated a place in a special school for the physically handicapped but was refusing to go there, insisting that he was not a wheelchair case like so many of the children. Jeanette arranged for him to go to Luke's school, which was specifically for delicate children.

Jeanette now turned her attention to Clare. She announced one day that there was no reason why the fourteen-year-old girl should not join the team of older members of the Family who had voluntarily undertaken the care of a severely disabled old lady in the neighbourhood.

'I can't do that!' Clare reiterated again and again. 'I'd be no good at it!'

But Jeanette persuaded her to try and to Clare's own surprise, she managed very well. As the weeks passed, the old lady became very fond of her. Clare was delighted with herself and gained a much needed degree of self-confidence. At home, she enjoyed taking care of the younger children, bathing them, reading to them, telling them stories. The hatred she had once had for herself began to diminish and she now showed signs of wanting affection from other people. She was also struggling to do well at school where, because of her earlier experiences, she was still lagging behind her contemporaries despite her latent ability.

The twins, Gary and Ellen, were also doing well at their private school, a small Christian establishment which disciplined the children by a system of merits and demerits. Gary, like any other twelve-year-old, had his fair share of naughtiness and on one memorable day, managed to earn himself an unacceptably high total of demerits, albeit for minor offences. He was sent to the headmaster for a caning.

By now, Jeanette become aware of a pressure group called

159

STOPP,* which had been campaigning to have corporal punishment in schools abolished. Before Gary had started going to the school, Jeanette had spent an hour with the headmaster, explaining to him how detrimental caning could be for the boy following the earlier abuse he had suffered. Despite the headmaster's guarantee that the boy would not be physically chastised, Gary arrived home with his back and buttocks so marked that Jeanette was shocked by the severity of his punishment. He was clearly in pain and walked with difficulty.

Without hesitation, she drove to the school and demanded an explanation for the severity of the damage the headmaster had inflicted. He offered no apology and showed no regret. Jeanette was appalled. This was a privately run Christian school, supposedly employing sympathetic, caring adults; yet they were condoning brutal beatings of young children.

She drove home, collected Gary and took him round to the Social Services Department. The shocked social worker instructed Jeanette to take Gary to their doctor, who, in turn, asked Jeanette to press charges against the headmaster immediately. Meanwhile, he reported the beating to the police, who took photographs of Gary's injuries and, like the doctor, asked Jeanette to press charges. Meanwhile, the Social Services workers went round to the school, from which they returned convinced that the man was suffering from religious mania.

Jeanette was by now in no doubt that the headmaster should be prevented from inflicting similar damage to another child, but her concern for Gary caused her to hesitate. After all he had been through in his early childhood, she did not now want him dragged through the Courts, as would be inevitable if the headmaster were prosecuted. She discussed the matter with Gary and it was finally agreed between them that she would take no further action against the man, but reluctantly would remove Gary from the school.

Unfortunately, this decision meant also removing Gary's twin, Ellen, and, even more unfortunately, the brain-damaged

*Society of Teachers Opposed to Physical Punishment. They were instrumental in getting the clauses abolishing corporal punishment for all children being educated at the public expense, included in the 1986 Education Bill.

160

child, Brian, who had newly started at the otherwise excellent school and had settled down very well. But Jeanette did not regret her decision, although all three children were sorry to leave, for she now discovered belatedly that Brian, too, had been beaten on his bare buttocks although not so severely as Gary.

It was nearing the end of the autumn term and four months since Brian had joined the Family with his brothers Ted and Roger. Jeanette had noticed that he was frequently bumping into things and took him to an eye specialist who diagnosed the boy as being only partially sighted and prescribed special glasses. Brian at once showed signs of far greater self-confidence as he moved around the house. Jeanette studied him more closely and came to the conclusion that he was not nearly as helpless as he appeared. His brothers did far more for him than she thought necessary.

She told him that he must make the effort to do things for himself. He denied he could manage even the simplest task.

'I can't do it!' he would say. 'I'm spastic! I can't do that, I'm brain damaged!'

She held a family conference and told the children that from now on, Brian was expected to do things for himself explaining the reasons for her decision. Within a matter of weeks, Brian began to reveal his capacity for independence.

Jeanette reported this to the educational psychologist and obtained his agreement that the boy should be reassessed. He was, of course, many years behind his contemporaries at reading and writing, and his social behaviour remained a serious problem, both at the school and at home. He was sexually provocative towards the girls and masturbated in front of them.

Jeanette found it extremely difficult to accept this particular child. Quite often, she would wake in the night to find him standing by her bed masturbating. While she was well aware that Brian was in no way responsible for his behaviour, she found these sexual advances horrifying because of her own childhood experiences. The fear that had once engulfed her as a child when she had woken to find her father standing by her bed returned with distressing force. It required every ounce of self-control to prevent herself shouting at the boy or hitting out at him, and to keep her voice quiet and controlled as she told him to stop what he was doing and go back to his room.

Jeanette had to make deliberate efforts to overcome her revulsion. Because she was afraid that her own feelings might somehow influence her attitude towards Brian's future upbringing, she had frequent consultations with his social worker. She strove to remain calm when Brian came up behind her, and voiced some lewd suggestion, and she tried to explain to him quietly that this kind of behaviour was unacceptable to her and would be to other females. She was aware that the unhappy boy needed to know that, despite her physical rejection of him, she cared about him, but it was not easy for her to show this damaged child affection.

Unfortunately, Brian had another trait which was far from endearing; a compulsive eater, he stuffed himself with food until he vomited on the floor. Jeanette tried to regulate his meals, but he resorted to stealing food, hiding it in his clothes, under his bed, amongst his toys. Several times, she caught him creeping down the stairs at night to raid the larder or the fridge, and she realised he was not going to be easily cured of this particular habit.

Roger was astonished to see Brian managing for himself. He felt a great weight had been lifted off his shoulders now that he knew he and Ted would not always be needed to look after their brother. Roger himself was still plagued by fears, not just his terrifying nightmares of being changed into a stick like Ted, but of reprisals by his parents if they discovered that he and his brothers had settled down in their foster home. His fears were confused by guilt because he was disobeying his parents' instructions. Physically strong, he hit out at the other children at home and at school whenever his uncertainties led him to violent temper tantrums.

But gradually, in long talks, Jeanette was helping him to understand what family relationships should be, employing the technique of using dolls to explain the normal behaviour of a mother and father towards each other and towards their children. At night, when he woke from his nightmares, she would take him into her own room, show him in her mirror that he really was still Roger, a ten-year-old boy, and not a walking stick. She would sit with him on her lap, holding the sobbing

162

child until he fell asleep. Fortunately, his personality was very endearing and, despite his behaviour, everyone, including his teachers, liked him.

Ted was proving more of a problem by virtue of his reticence. If Jeanette came into a room, he would walk out of it. If she put a hand on his arm, he would actually retch – even vomit. Jeanette felt as if she were in some way contaminated until she discovered the reason for his behaviour. One day, she walked into the bathroom unaware that Ted was in there. He had forgotten to lock the door. As she was on the point of apologising, Ted grabbed a bath towel and quickly covered his body, but his expression was not that of embarrassment – it was one of acute fear.

Jeanette could not believe he was afraid she would hurt him. A moment later she understood – that he thought she was about to make sexual advances to him; that now she had become his mother he was expecting her to behave towards him as his own mother had done. Her reaction was one of anger at the terrible injury Ted's parents had inflicted on their innocent offspring. Ted was fifteen years old and she wondered how long it would be – if ever – before such a horrifying expectation of parental behaviour was wiped from his mind.

She had heard many people express the view that parents like Ted's must be mentally ill. She did not accept that theory. No doctor or psychiatrist had diagnosed them as mentally sick. Such people demanded from life gratification of their desires regardless of the cost. Ted's parents had been well aware that they were doing wrong when they had involved their three sons in their sexual orgies. To have hidden behind closed doors out of sight of eyes they knew would condemn them, was in itself an admission of guilt. Perhaps the greatest harm the parents had done was to bring up the boys to believe that their behaviour was normal. Children naturally adopted their parents' concepts of right and wrong and these three boys, living now with a totally new concept of normality, were hopelessly confused.

Ted listened carefully as Jeanette tried to explain that real mother-love was an emotional and not a physical thing, but she was far from certain that she had convinced him. For fifteen years, he had been taught differently and clearly he did not find it easy to adjust his ideas. But as time went by, he no longer left the room when she entered it. Although she was certain that he ceased to fear she would rape him if she had the opportunity, he still kept his distance.

That autumn Jeanette arranged for Sylvie to attend an adult training centre with Neal; but since all they were given to occupy them for five hours a day was the simple task of putting things into boxes, they both became bored and depressed. She then found Sylvie a job washing up in a nearby old people's home. For a while, Sylvie enjoyed it. Although her behaviour was often strange, she knew how to behave herself socially and was struggling very hard to learn to read – a skill she was unable to accomplish, much to her distress. Now twenty-two, she had begun to take an interest in boys, and in particular in an educationally subnormal boy of the same age. The boy's mother disapproved of the friendship but Jeanette encouraged him to visit Sylvie, who greatly enjoyed the Family's gentle mocking about her 'boyfriend'. She knew that it was normal for a girl of her age to fall in love, and she wanted to be like Natalie who was about to marry her boyfriend – a young painter and decorator called Tim.

Jasper, who was eight, was now deemed able by the psychologist, to attend a special school. The local authority suggested several which were primarily for autistic children. Sadly, many of the children Jeanette saw in these schools were unable to do more than lie on the floor banging their heads, and this was the very last example she wanted for Jasper, who tended now to imitate what he saw around him. She insisted that the authority should come up with an alternative type of school for Jasper since, whilst severely retarded and still unable to talk, he was certainly not autistic.

Finally, a health visitor suggested a school in Walthamstow catering for children with educational problems. However, she warned Jeanette that since it was outside their area, Jasper was unlikely to get a place there. Undaunted Jeanette went at once to visit the school and, instantly impressed, talked them into putting Jasper on their two-year waiting list. The local authority were not prepared for him to wait that long, but the school jumped him to the top of their list and it now remained only for daily transport to be arranged. This took a further six months. But the wait was well worthwhile since Jasper settled down there quickly and happily.

Jeanette still had responsibility for the borough *Be My Parent* book containing photographs of difficult-to-place children in need of parents. One particular photograph of two Down's Syndrome babies seemed always to be drawing itself to her attention and she was beginning to fear that these twins were never going to be found a home. She put the photograph on the mantelshelf so that when prospective parents came to see the book, she would remember first to mention the unwanted babies.

There were persistent demands from the Family that the two-year-old twins should come to live with them. The babies' social worker invited Jeanette to go down to Wales to see the children, Owen and Philip, and Jeanette decided at once to foster them. She had noted how their former foster mother catered to their every need, and resolved to reverse this situation – as she had with Brian – to enable them to become more independent.

It was several days before Owen and Phil settled down and stopped screaming whenever they wanted attention or when they were put in their cots at night. The children were worried about their constant crying, but Jeanette was adamant that the twins must be taught that this was not the way to achieve their desires. They were physically retarded for their age, but they could pull themselves across the floor on their stomachs. Now, stimulated by the constant activity around them, they quickly began to make progress.

The Family, accustomed to Neal, Brian and Sylvie's often bizarre behaviour accepted the twins as they would any other very young children, and vied with each other to cuddle and play with them. Jeanette hoped that before long, she would be able to adopt them.

One summer evening when the Family were gathered round the television, an advertisement suddenly appeared picturing, amongst others the three boys, Ted, Brian and Roger, and stating that they needed good homes. It was part of a scheme now in operation whereby agencies were allowed to advertise for adopting parents for the children they were trying to place. The children's photographs could appear in magazines or brochures and on television. The boys sat staring at their own faces in silent horror. Had Jeanette decided after all that she did not want to keep them in her family? Brian looked confused, Ted looked appalled and Roger, who was holding a cup in his hand, threw it violently across the room and burst into tears.

Jeanette's heart filled with anger at this bureaucratic blunder. Hurriedly she attempted to reassure them that this was no more than an unfortunate oversight on the part of the adoption agency responsible for them; that they must have forgotten to remove the boys' names from the lists of children in need of homes. She was bitter at such carelessness, which temporarily undermined the boys' still tentative trust in her. In due course, someone came down from the adoption agency to apologise to the boys, but it was many weeks before they were entirely convinced.

During that same summer, Neal's adoption was finalised. Jeanette was anxious to become his legal guardian because after the age of eighteen he would no longer be officially 'In Care' and there would be no one responsible for securing his future.

She had reached the conclusion that it would not be in Ben's interest to adopt him, too. As a trained nurse, she knew the course that muscular dystrophy invariably took, and that Ben would eventually need both special equipment and the extra financial allowance made for such cases – advantages that, as his adoptive mother, she herself could not afford to supply. Fortunately, Jeanette's relationship with Ben had progressed to a point where they could talk openly and with mutual confidence. It was enough for him, he now said, to know that she considered him as her son and would have adopted him if she had felt it best for him.

'I can change my name by Deed Poll when I'm eighteen,' he said.

Quite by chance Jeanette had discovered the previous year that he had no idea of what was wrong with him. Passing the bathroom door one morning soon after they had moved into Campbell Road, she heard him crying. When he let her in, she asked him to tell her what was the matter.

166

'You don't understand,' he said when he could control his voice. 'All the other kids are getting bigger and I'm getting smaller. I can see myself in the mirror – I'm getting thinner all the time!'

'But Ben, that is only to be expected. It's part of your illness,' she explained gently, before realising from the blank expression of incomprehension on his face that he had no idea what she was talking about.

It had never been Jeanette's policy with her children to be other than honest and she could see no virtue now in trying to conceal from the fifteen-year-old that he had muscular dystrophy. As compassionately as she could, she explained the nature of the disease and that there was no known cure for it.

'You mean I could be dead in a year from now?'

'No, I'm not saying that you have only a year to live, Ben. I am saying that you have many days of life left and that you must live every single one of them to the full. You must fight your illness, not give way to it. We'll fight it together. There'll be times when you are frightened, but you can tell me about them and there will be two of us to tackle it.'

'They told me I'd soon need a wheelchair,' he said. 'That's why they sent one with me when I came here.'

Jeanette's voice became firmer.

'I think that to some extent it will be up to you how long you can avoid the need for one,' she said. 'If you exercise those muscles as much and as often as possible, you may not need it for a long while.'

She steeled her heart against pity and told Ben he must have as much physical exercise as he could. To keep him from worrying too much about himself, she insisted that he went back to school.

It was far from easy for a young boy to have to accept at the age of fifteen that he was going to die. He tried to lead as normal a life as the other boys in the family, sharing their jokes, their companionship and even riding tandem with Ted and Jason when they went cycling. Nevertheless, there were times when Ben was depressed. The Family would endeavour to help him through such moments. Some days, however, his depression was too deep to be easily dispersed. Grieving for his lost health and for the loss of the future years he would never enjoy, he sobbed

167

in Jeanette's arms while she tried to revive his broken spirit by willing some of her own strength into him. Her suffering at such moments was as great as Ben's and he was aware that she grieved with him. His courage helped him through these bad times.

Whilst Jeanette's relationship with Ben had become open and frank, she was still experiencing awkwardness with Ted. Although she now knew why he felt so ill at ease in her company and that he was endeavouring to overcome it, he had clearly not yet done so. He was keeping her metaphorically as well as physically at arm's length. But during the summer following the year of his arrival, when they were once more at Farleys farmhouse in Sussex, Ted fell off his bike. His injuries were such that Jeanette had to drive him to hospital.

He was obviously in great pain and, instinctively, Jeanette held him as the doctor inspected the damage. In tears with the pain, Ted made no move to extricate himself from the comforting arms around him. When finally Jeanette drove him home, she knew that they had crossed a very important hurdle and that Ted had finally learned what real maternal love and care could mean.

Chapter 17

'In 1985 there was overall a 71.5% increase in the number of children registered for abuse other than physical injury and a 126.5% increase in those registered for sexual abuse.'
(Initial Findings, 1985, from NSPCC Register Research)

For the many years Jeanette had been closely associated with a number of small adoption agencies to whom she was often able to offer advice about the placement of a child. Prospective adopters were welcomed in Jeanette's home and when needed, advice would be given on the problems new parents might expect. Jeanette herself fostered several of the agencies' children, and the working relationship between her family and one of the the agencies had slowly developed into friendship. They went on outings and picnics arranged by the agency for adopting parents and their families; and their social workers frequently dropped in to see the children on a friendly basis.

That autumn, a member of the agency called Patricia, with whom Jeanette felt an unusual rapport over the care of children requested help with a twelve-year-old boy called Ray. The agency was anxious to find him parents, but his behaviour at the Children's Home where he had been all his childhood had regressed so badly that they wanted Jeanette to assess him over a period of three months to judge whether he would be acceptable to prospective parents.

Jeanette considered what was known about the boy. At the age of four his parents had separated. From that time on he was often picked up by the police approaching strange men in the street, asking, 'Are you my Daddy?' He was continually running away from home, his reason being that he wanted to find his father. Although his mother was willing to keep her other children, she rejected Ray, and, at the age of five, he was put 'In Care' and sent to a Children's Home. He continued to run away, on average twice a week, despite the fact that he had been reunited with his father who lived nearby. The man had remarried and although he was not antagonistic towards his son, neither he nor his new wife wished to have the boy to live with them. Ray remained in the Home, where his mother visited him, until he was twelve years old.

During those eight long years no one discovered why he ran away so often or what he did when he was absent, sometimes for several days before he was found. He was often violent but he was co-operative with the various workers who tried to psycho-analyse him, promising not to run away again, but then a few days later he would disappear.

Jeanette agreed to take the boy, curious now to discover what was motivating him. After he had been with her for a few days, convinced that there was an explanation for his behaviour, she telephoned the Home. A member of the staff told her that Ray was physically healthy, although he had complained occasionally of stomach ache and there had been reports of him bleeding from the rectum due to constipation.

'And the doctor gave him an anal examination?' Jeanette persisted. She could hardly believe her own ears when the answer she received was negative.

Jeanette now suspected that the boy might have been involved with homosexuals. She was seriously concerned about him. He had arrived at her house with a knife secreted about his person and hidden it under his pillow. When she had removed it, he had stolen knives from the kitchen and hidden them wherever he had thought they might remain undiscovered. She was convinced that he believed he needed a knife for his self-protection.

At first he resisted her demands that he tell her what he had been doing. But when he realised that she really was not going to let him leave the room until he confessed, he broke down and, sobbing, told her that for almost as long as he could remember, he had been involved in homosexual relationships. Under Jeanette's encouragement, he repeated his story to the social worker. Jeanette was convinced that he needed more professional help than she could give him, and permission was obtained from the Social Services for the boy to see a psychiatrist.

The agency had been making every effort to find suitable parents for Ray. But Jeanette was by now aware that neither fostering nor adoption were appropriate for him because of his many emotional problems. Patricia asked Jeanette if she would keep the boy for a year to see if there might be changes in his behaviour before a final decision was made; but Jeanette was unwilling to keep Ray on those terms. Either he left or he became a permanent member of the Family. He had already taken up an exceptionally large measure of her time and effort and would need a great deal more. She was by no means unaware of the boy's limitations, and that it would be many years before he could make long-term relationships. He had been too mentally damaged for that to be possible, but she was prepared to do her best if that was what Patricia wanted for Ray.

It was finally agreed that he would be fostered by Jeanette on a permanent basis.

Meanwhile, Ray ran away again and was once more returned by the police. Acting upon a hunch, Jeanette ordered him to strip and saw that he was badly bruised and bleeding from the rectum. She immediately telephoned his social worker – without whose permission she could not get the boy medically examined – stating that she was now certain he had been with homosexuals.

The social worker decided to wait for more concrete evidence. Not long afterwards, Ray again ran away, this time for five nights. Jeanette drove round to Ray's home, supposing that he might be at his mother's. There was a man walking up and down outside the house, dressed all in white and acting oddly, appeared to be sniffing drugs from his handkerchief. He must have noticed her presence and quickly disappeared from sight. Shortly after Ray's return a few nights later, Jeanette saw

171

the same man waiting at their own gate. Bravely, she and Lucy went out to confront him, demanding an explanation for his presence. He walked off without giving a reply. Very uneasy, they sat up all night, but he did not reappear. She was now convinced that he had been waiting for Ray.

Ray vanished yet again and after several days was picked up by the police at the seaside. Jeanette alerted his social worker and they went together to the police station to collect him. Ray had violently resisted the police and as a consequence, they had removed his shoes so that he could not kick them with any effect. Since he was wearing no socks, Jeanette noticed at once that the soles of the boy's feet were covered in bruises, as was his face.

'Look – just look at his feet – at his face and hands!' she said to the social worker. They drove Ray home. His social worker refused to come indoors, saying that it was late and she must get back. She ignored Jeanette's protests that she should be present when Jeanette took Ray upstairs to examine him and left promising to telephone later that evening.

As Jeanette had anticipated, Ray's whole body was black and blue with bruises. She immediately telephoned the agency, requesting permission for Ray to be medically examined by a police doctor. The fostering regulations did not allow her to take such a step unilaterally. She explained that she was convinced Ray had been homosexually assaulted, and the agency promised to telephone her back.

She sat by the telephone waiting. At ten o'clock that Friday night, having still received no call, she rang the home number of the agency field worker, Maria, only to be told that no one had been able to contact Ray's social worker and the matter would have to wait until morning. At eleven o'clock next morning, Jeanette had heard nothing and when she telephoned, was told first that she must wait until the afternoon; then until the evening; then until after the weekend.

Jeanette decided to take matters into her own hands. She telephoned her friend Peter Stickings, Ray's headmaster, and explained the situation. He tried to get positive action from the Social Services, but failing to do so, he rang the police. The Chief Inspector said they would examine the boy but that

Jeanette should not delay beyond the following morning or it could be too late to obtain concrete evidence.

On Monday morning, Maria and Ray's social worker arrived at Jeanette's house, but refused Jeanette permission to take Ray to the police station. It was now over forty-eight hours since Jeanette had first reported Ray's condition and her suspicions to them. Mindful of the Inspector's warning and well aware that she was acting outside the limits of her authority, Jeanette turned to Ray.

'On your feet, Ray,' she said. 'We're going!'

With the two social workers protesting as they followed her, Jeanette walked Ray to the police station where, at long last, he was examined by a doctor.

'Your suspicions are justified,' he told Jeanette. 'The boy has been used by homosexuals not once but many times. He is badly scarred. May I have your permission to take photographs of the injuries?'

Jeanette, as a foster mother, was perfectly willing to give it but did not have the authority to do so. However, having established that Ray had no objections to the procedure, the doctor promptly made the necessary arrangements.

Before they all left the police station, the police officer announced that there would be an official investigation. Ray had made a statement implicating a Mr X, he said. It appeared that there had been some sort of homosexual racket going on for years and that there would now have to be an investigation.

'Now you are going to *have* to do something!' Jeanette said bitterly to the two social workers.

In the next few days, Ray told Jeanette that many years previously, when he was at the Home, he and a number of other children had been picked up as they had come out of Sunday school. The man he identified as Mr X had taken them back to, Ray's own, home where pornographic photographs were taken of them and various forms of sexual abuse had taken place. Jeanette learned from the police inspector that the Juvenile Bureau would be involved in view of the boy's age.

She was in little doubt that the Social Services Department were furious with her, since, by taking matters into her own hands, she had uncovered this hornets' nest. She could well

173

believe that they would be reluctant to have such a shocking case investigated since Ray was 'In Care' and therefore the responsibility of the local authority. A few days later, the local police notified Jeanette that regrettably, Ray's case had been transferred to the borough who had first received him into 'Care', and that their responsibility for the case had therefore ended.

Jeanette promptly telephoned the relevant Chief Inspector, who invited her to meet him the following afternoon. On her arrival at exactly the appointed time, she discovered that a senior social worker from the new borough was present, but no one from the adoption agency. Moreover, the discussion about Ray had already taken place.

'We've decided not to take the matter any further,' the police officer informed her after introducing her to the social worker. 'We all know that Ray is a perpetual liar and we've agreed that he could be making up the whole story.'

Jeanette could not believe her ears.

'But the doctor has examined him, seen the bruises, reported that the boy's rectum is full of scars...'

The man's eyes avoided hers.

'They could have been caused by a stick – he could have put a stick up his rectum.'

'I'll never believe that this boy injured himself!' she declared. 'For one thing there were bruises on his hips and buttocks and the position of those hand marks were such that Ray could not have made them himself.'

'I agree!' the officer admitted. 'But we've only the boy's word as to who is responsible and since we've not been able to trace the fellow, we have nobody to charge with the offence.'

Jeanette was speechless – and very, very angry. Because of the delay over having Ray examined, it had been too late to take a test to see if there had been semen present in his rectum. When she found her voice, she put forward every argument she could. Ray had been able to describe the man. They even knew his name! But to no avail. Jeanette's frustration knew no bounds and was accompanied by anger and fear for the children now in the Home who, since nothing was being done, were presumably still at risk.

She reminded the Inspector of an excellent drawing of Mr X that Ray, a talented artist, had done, and how true a likeness it was to the man she had seen.

'That wouldn't hold up as evidence,' he said immediately. 'Lots of parents have been known to make things up in defence of their children...'

Frustrated and defeated, Jeanette could see no other way to convince the police that Ray had not been lying. She was very disturbed by the effect all this was having on the boy, and was glad that he was shortly to see the psychiatrist at the London Hospital since she herself was far from sure that she was competent to counsel Ray who obviously had homosexual tendencies.

Jeanette and Joyce were both now deeply concerned lest the Social Services removed Ray because she had gone against their advice and taken him to see the police surgeon to be medically examined. However, before the Social Services could take such a step, Ray's mother took it into her head to have her son made a ward of Court – an option open to her if she had valid reasons for requesting it. This effectively removed him from the jurisdiction of the Social Services; but Jeanette now needed the Court's permission to arrange psychiatric help for him – inevitably a lengthy procedure. She had no alternative, meanwhile, but to cancel his appointments at the London Hospital.

Despite the distress and frustrations of the past few months, there were happy highlights for the Family in the same period. In January, Natalie's first baby was born and she named it after Jeanette's first adopted baby, Wendy. In February, Clare's adoption was finalised and plans had been put in motion for Ted, Brian and Roger to be adopted before Ted's eighteenth birthday the following year. All three boys were now anxious to cut their links with their parents and were learning to accept the new values and ideals Jeanette was teaching them, although it was not always easy for them.

Jasper, now nine years old, was slowly making progress and had begun to speak, although he had not as yet acquired the ability to converse. He used only a few words but he understood nearly everything that was said to him and would obey very simple instructions. He was also beginning to use the word 'toilet' and, provided someone heard him and took him to the lavatory in time, remained dry during the day.

Physically, too, he had made great progress and was healthy although hyperactive. He now ran around playing with his toys, and he had finally learned to dress himself. He could also feed and bath himself although not without supervision. With the exception of Wendy, he did not attempt to play with the other children. If told by Jeanette to do so, he would sit still, but the moment she left the room he would make his escape. Despite the other children's efforts to include him, he would never join in their group activities, but even with these limitations, it was rewarding enough to see him a physical equal to his peers – something no one would have thought possible four years ago when he had been found in his cot close to death.

That spring, the whole Family were thrown into a state of great excitement. The Springboard Housing Association had heard of a large, convent in Essex which would accommodate them all with room to spare. Situated on the outskirts of a remote hamlet called East Hanningfield, there were nevertheless local schools available and special schools not too far distant in Chelmsford. Jeanette discussed the possibility with her children, who were as eager as she to live in the country. Jeanette was conscious of the fact that she had the indefatigable Ken Start to thank for this wonderful offer of a large country home for the Family. Over the years he had befriended them practically and financially on many occasions. As Director of the Springboard Housing Association, he was in the unique position of being able to persuade them not only to offer the Family the use of the convent, but to agree that there would be no rent asked.

The Association had been invited to manage the whole of the St Giles Trust estate, which included the erstwhile isolation hospital now sheltering a number of former lepers and another large four-bedroomed cottage called St Marie's as well as The Old Convent, its garden and the surrounding fields. The elderly nuns living in the convent were moving in a few weeks' time, their task of nursing the patients in the hospital having come to an end some years earlier.

With growing enthusiasm, Ken Start discussed his plans and hopes with Jeanette. At present, staff were employed to care for the ex-patients and many of the jobs they did could be undertaken by Jeanette, Joyce and the older children. Lucy, who was an efficient cook, could be given a small cabin in the grounds to live in and could take over the kitchens; the older boys could repair and redecorate St Marie's which, it was hoped, would soon be occupied. Joyce, who was thinking of taking early retirement from her full-time job so that she could help Jeanette with her ever-growing family, could do administrative work for the Association and supervise the care of the St Giles residents, for which she would receive a small remuneration.

Jeanette herself would continue to be responsible for her children and would oversee the liaison between the two Christian communities, young and old. They would become one big happy family, the younger members benefitting from the inclusion of 'grandparents', the lonely older members benefitting by the advent of 'grandchildren'. Not least, Ken said enthusiastically, the children could share the facilities already available to the old people, such as the pottery room, the snooker table and the laundry room with its modern machinery.

Jeanette was moved by so much generosity, all due to her friend's concern for her and the Family. The reserve which had dominated her childhood had never left her and she had always found it difficult to relate to other adults, even Joyce with whom she had been so closely aligned for so many years. But with Ken she felt a deep empathy mixed with gratitude and she had come to look upon him as a true brother, spiritually as well as practically.

Joyce had long since forgotten her earlier concerns that the Family should not attempt to move to the country. There were now eighteen children to be cared for and even though the older ones took care of most of the domestic work between them on a rota system, Jeanette was often greatly in need during the day of another adult pair of hands. Joyce had no hesitation in approving Ken Start's plans and resigning from her job. Jeanette accepted the Springboard offer and they were told that if there were no bureaucratic hitches, they might be able to move to the country before the end of the year. That autumn, however, was to be one of the unhappiest Jeanette and the Family had known. Long before they moved, there were repercussions as a result of her clash with the authorities concerning Ray.

A case conference was now convened to discuss Ray's future. A representative from the Court was in attendance. Jeanette's desire for the boy to be seen by an independent assessor was opposed by the adoption agency. Jeanette stressed the point that a complete outsider would be able to make a more objective assessment of Ray than would someone who had been previously involved.

Since this seemed reasonable, the Court representative invited the agency to give their reasons why they were insisting upon having their own psychiatrist. Their reply was that he was the man *they* had chosen and that it was not Jeanette's right to go against their recommendations. The agency was overruled and Jeanette was told the Court would arrange for Ray to see an independent psychiatrist as a matter of urgency.

Immediately following this case and without explanation the agency withdrew all Jeanette's children from their books. They refused to answer her letters or telephone calls. She discussed this extraordinary turn of events endlessly with Joyce. Was this the direct result of her taking unilateral action over Ray's physical examination by the police? Or was the agency resenting the implication that they had not been acting in Ray's best interest by opposing her desire for an independent assessment? Alternatively, was it possible they felt that their control of the whole situation was being challenged?

Jeanette could not believe at that point in time that the rift between the agency and the Family was irrevocable. They had worked together effectively and with wonderful results for so long, it was inconceivable that the present situation would not eventually blow over.

Meanwhile she was left without support for the seven children in her care. They, in turn, were left without social workers. The repercussions upon Ted, Brian and Roger were particularly distressing. The withdrawal of their social worker from their case meant that the current application for their adoption by Jeanette would be quashed.

178

By the time she had come to terms with the situation, it was too late to find them an alternative social worker who might have been able to arrange their adoption before Ted's eighteenth birthday. The boys were heartbroken. Jeanette and Joyce were at a loss to explain the situation to them since they did not understand it themselves. Jeanette herself was not only bewildered, but furiously angry. Whatever the reasons or feelings which had motivated the agency's decision that the rift should be final, their actions could not be justified given the effects upon the children. Without explanation, they had withdrawn their support and cooperation at a time when the children were struggling to adjust to new concepts; to trust adults; to find security. It was not simply that Ted had lost the security his adoption by Jeanette would have afforded him; but that every single child now felt their position within the Family was a precarious one, their stability at the whim of social workers who could, without explanation, affect their future lives.

A senior social worker with a field worker came to see them. The agency, he told Jeanette, had refused her request for an explanation. The Department had received a letter from them inferring that the blame for the rift lay at Jeanette's door, not theirs; that she was 'too difficult to work with'.

'To be quite honest with you, Jeanette,' he concluded, 'I think the way the agency has behaved to you and the children is bloody appalling!'

The senior social worker showed Jeanette a letter written by the agency. 'Support of the kind we are offering can only be effective if there is mutual trust . . . and it had become apparent that what we offer was not what Jeanette wanted . . .'

She had always welcomed and needed support, Jeanette thought bitterly. As for the lack of mutual trust, it seemed that the agency were ignoring the fact that where Ray had been concerned, it was *they* who had betrayed it. To have permitted a seriously sexually abused child to go unexamined for two and a half days was good enough reason surely for *her* trust in *them* to be undermined.

It was not simply that they had made a very grave mistake, Jeanette said sadly to Joyce, but they had lacked the courage to admit it, which would have enabled them to continue their

179

mutual association for the children's benefit. Instead, they had opted out and, as Jeanette had so often witnessed, it was the children who suffered.

The unhappy incident now resolved into a strengthening of her determination that she would do everything in her power to ensure that bureaucratic bungling should never again harm one single child in her care.

Chapter 18

'Stress factors precipitating abuse by parents varied depending upon the type of abuse. Marital problems were recorded most often for sexual and emotional abuse cases, for the children who failed to thrive and for those who were thought to be at serious risk of abuse. External stress factors such as unemployment, debt and poor housing were recorded frequently. (Initial Findings, 1985, from NSPCC Register Research)

Several years previously, Jeanette's family had come to the attention of a film producer by the name of Nigel Evans. He was interested in children and had already made a documentary film called *Where Love Starts*, which included Mick, the ten-year-old boy Jeanette had persistently rescued from the East End homosexual haunts. Nigel had never forgotten Jeanette's comment that she felt English people had never in their hearts accepted children's importance in society; that they preferred to live in ignorance of the gross injustices and cruelty inflicted on the young. He was now anxious to make another film which he would call *Taking the Lid Off* in an attempt to publicise the sufferings and needs of children like Jeanette's.

As always, Jeanette discussed the suggestion with the Family. They were all agreed that whilst it would mean certain aspects of their backgrounds would have to be made public, the film could prove of immense benefit to all those children who had not been fortunate enough to find caring homes and parents.

Jeanette believed very strongly that unless the public were made aware of the truth, the apathy towards child care could not improve.

When in August, Jeanette and the Family went down to the farmhouse for the annual six weeks summer holiday, Nigel Evans and his film crew went with them, staying in a small hotel nearby. They became such familiar figures that the Family hardly noticed their presence. The whole crew often joined in their activities and almost became members of the large cheerful family.

There was only one unhappy child during those warm, sunny days – an eleven-year-old girl called Susie who the local authority had placed in Jeanette's care for six weeks prior to her going to a permanent foster home.

The little girl had long, dark untidy hair half concealing a thin, pointed face, and large, sad, blue eyes. She seemed bewildered by her strange surroundings and was frequently in tears. At night, she would wake screaming from some terrible nightmare, and after bathing her and changing the wet sheets on the child's bed, Jeanette would sit with her, trying as best she could to reassure her and gain her confidence.

For once, the deep emotional disturbances of a sexually abused child like Susie surfaced quickly and late one night, two weeks after her arrival, Susie told Jeanette her story. Haltingly, accompanied by many tears, the heart-breaking tale emerged:

'I lived with my Mum until I was three and then I was put in a Home in Essex. Then I was fostered by a family but I had rows with the kids there. The Mum was nice but I didn't really know the Dad. I went to school but I was always in trouble and the school said they wouldn't keep me and then the family said they wouldn't keep me so I was moved to a Children's Home in London. It was full of teenagers and people older than me.'

Jeanette wondered now who could have placed a seven-year-old child in a Home where there was no one remotely close to her own age.

'I went to school, with them – a special school,' Susie told her. 'There was bars on the windows and all the doors was locked, and when we wanted to go to the toilet, the classroom doors was unlocked and we was taken to the toilet and then the

182

toilet doors had to be unlocked and they waited outside 'til we'd finished. Then we was brought back and locked in the classroom again.'

The girl went on to say that at playtime, the children were locked outside even in the cold of winter. There had always been a teacher stationed at the school gate to ensure that no one got out of the playground. Small wonder the child now said that she would never ever forget all the locked doors! In the Children's Home, Susie had no one to play with although there was one other girl who was fourteen – twice her age – who befriended her. But it was the behaviour of the boys that had so deeply affected the child.

'There was one boy who went out to work,' she told Jeanette. 'He stole pens and paper from work and brought them back and said to us girls "I'll give you these if you let me touch you." He took us into the cupboard and touched us. He touched me so many times I've lost count. There was another boy who was older. He had curly hair. He took me into the shower room and locked it. I tried to get out but he kept me in there...'

Horrified to hear that such a thing was possible within the protection of a Children's Home, Jeanette learned that the boy had raped Susie who was, after the five years she had spent there, still only eleven years old.

'I was scared!' Susie said. 'I screamed and the staff came and knocked on the door and the boy unlocked it. But it was too late 'cos he'd already done it. So he was sent away and there was a lot of fuss, but the other boys still went on doing it until I got sent to you.'

She clung to Jeanette, clearly desperately in need to belong to someone, and very frightened. She was afraid that one of the boys would come into her room at night and begged Jeanette to have a bolt put on the door. She herself pulled furniture in front of the door in case one of the bigger boys in the Family tried to get in. Jeanette said what she could to reassure her that no such thing could happen and that the boys in the Family would all respect her privacy.

Perhaps because of Susie's many years spent in the company of teenagers, she dressed like a girl of seventeen or eighteen, and she had also unconsciously adopted a sexually provocative

183

manner which – since she was so terrified of sex – was very misleading.

Her response to Jeanette's care and counselling was immediate. The child began to trust her and to feel safe in the family environment, and she pleaded to be allowed to stay on a permanent basis. Susie was convinced that once the new foster parents learned of her past they could not possibly love her; that everything that had happened was her fault and that no one else but Jeanette would understand that she had not meant to do anything bad or 'rude'. Whilst the filming was still taking place, Susie was often to be found clinging to Jeanette, tears streaming down her cheeks at the thought of the unknown foster family to whom she would shortly be despatched.

As fate would have it, the foster parents suddenly changed their minds about the little girl. Her social worker came down to see her to explain the situation to her. In tears once more, Susie begged to be allowed to remain with Jeanette. Impressed by the obvious improvements in her physical and mental health during the last few weeks, her social worker agreed to put the suggestion forward at a departmental meeting, but warned her that she must not raise her hopes too high. After he had left, Susie became almost hysterical. It was some time before Jeanette could calm her but the child remained tearful and full of trepidation for her future.

Shortly before their return to London, Susie's social worker telephoned to say that it had been agreed that Jeanette should become Susie's new foster mother. Nigel had managed to film several sequences of Jeanette's counselling of Susie and was able to celebrate this happy ending to the summer holiday with the Family.

By now he had learned of the proposed move to Essex. He had listened to Jeanette and Joyce discussing the various ways young and old could benefit each other, and felt drawn into their enthusiasm. Here were two women whose unswerving faith carried them beyond their financial difficulties and their already heavy work-load, to consider the loneliness of an isolated, elderly community. He decided to include the removal from London to make a second film called *In the Name of Charity* which would highlight the planned union between the Family and the old folk.

Ken Start now informed them that not only need the Family pay no rent for The Old Convent, but that they could also forget fuel and electricity bills. Jeanette and Joyce were overcome by this generous offer and the whole family celebrated.

Soon after they had returned to Campbell Road after the summer holidays, Jeanette attended the wedding of Betsy's daughter. Nearly all the members of her family were present, including, inevitably, her father. He was now seventy years old and, so he told her during the reception, he had not long to live – in fact, a month or two at most. It was a warm, sunny day and he asked Jeanette if she would go outside with him for a short while so that they could talk privately.

Jeanette had seen him very rarely although his second wife had several times tried to effect a reconciliation and had twice accompanied him on visits to Jeanette's house – visits Jeanette had not welcomed. Since their mother had died in 1981 her brothers and sister had met him infrequently when he had attended family occasions. Sitting beside him, uneasy and with many misgivings, Jeanette waited for him to explain why he wanted to see her alone.

It was not long before he turned to face her saying that he had terminal cancer. Jeanette felt the same pity for her father as for anyone with cancer, but there was no deep sense of impending loss.

'Will you forgive me?' he asked, his face now thin and drawn with age and illness. His expression combined both embarrassment and anxiety.

All that was most compassionate in Jeanette's nature longed to be able to give her father the answer that he wanted, but memories of her childhood and all that she had suffered because of his behaviour – not only as a child, but as an adult – welled up into her mind. She would not lie to him.

'What do you mean by forgiveness?' she asked. 'Are you asking me to say that I condone what happened?'

He made no reply.

'I could say to you: "It's all right! It doesn't matter!" but it wouldn't be the truth.'

'I have been told I have only two months to live,' he reminded her.

'That doesn't change anything,' Jeanette replied. 'What

185

happened can't be changed. I don't hate you any more, but we aren't talking about hate, are we? I don't feel anything for you but pity.' She paused briefly before she went on: 'Now can I ask you something? As a child, I was told you were sick ... but you weren't, were you?'

He agreed that he had not been suffering from any mental illness – an acknowledgement by a parent which Jeanette had always considered of great importance when she was counselling her children. Social workers had often told children that the parents who had abused them were 'sick' and this quite frequently led to misunderstandings, the child assuming that if one of their parents was mentally ill, then they themselves might have inherited the 'disease'.

Ted was suffering at the present time from just such a conviction. She was finding it very hard to explain to him that parents such as his could very rarely be categorised medically as 'mentally ill', that most people who sexually abused children were consciously doing wrong, that a child therefore had no need to feel inadequate or guilty. Ted had no need to pretend to himself or to others that his parents' behaviour was excusable. She herself had spent many agonised hours in her childhood feeling that somehow she had been responsible for her father's sexual abuse. It had taken a very long time to rid herself of those feelings of guilt and the accompanying loss of self-worth. For this alone, she could never forgive him.

He died in November. Her brother, Alan, attended the funeral but Jeanette felt it would be hypocritical of her to mourn someone she had never loved. Alan, like her mother and sister, had refused to acknowledge – or even discuss – the crime her father had committed. Whilst not denying it, they chose not to think or talk about it. Jeanette believed that because it was easier for Alan, he chose to put their father on a pedestal. At the funeral, which Jeanette steadfastly refused to attend despite Alan's pleas, he asked the Minister to state that his father had been a 'devoted family man who idolised his children'. Jeanette deplored such a hypocritical eulogy and felt totally alienated by Alan's attitude.

She was far more deeply affected by the approaching death of a woman called Amy Milligan whom a Quaker friend had asked her to visit in the hospice where she lay dying of cancer. Plans had been made for her three boys, Greg, Jeff and two-year-old Adrian, to be fostered after her death; but she was unhappy about the fostering arrangements. Since a recent meeting with Jeanette, she was desperately anxious that her children should join the Family.

Despite Amy's rapidly deteriorating condition, she begged Jeanette to drive her to her home where the eldest boy, Greg, was doing his best to keep the family going. At seventeen, he should have been at school, but had remained at home to take care of little Adrian. To ease the situation, Jeanette had been caring for the toddler on a daily basis until final decisions were made for the boys. With drugs strapped to her body feeding through a tube directly into a vein, the dying woman was miraculously free of pain as Jeanette and Joyce drove her at her request to her home. They had been warned that the exertion could kill her but she was determined to be the one to tell the boys in the privacy of her own home that she was dying and that it was her last wish that they should go to live with Jeanette.

Very soon after that visit, Amy died. Jeanette was with her when she lapsed into a coma which lasted forty-eight hours. When the end came, Jeanette was formally advised by Amy's solicitor that in her will, Amy had appointed her, Jeanette Elizabeth Roberts, sole guardian of her three children.

'Is this legal?' Jeanette asked. 'Can someone leave their children to a person in their will?'

'It is as legal as an adoption,' was the reply she received.

The two older boys deferred to their mother's last wishes – but reluctantly – and were determined that Jeanette should know it. Greg convinced that Jeanette was trying to usurp his place with his brothers was quietly angry and unco-operative. Jeff, aged thirteen, was arrogant, violent and had a vicious temper. He had been expelled from his school for hitting one teacher and pushing another into a window. He believed he put a jinx on everything and anyone he came in contact with, and even blamed himself when the family cat killed his hamster! The two-year-old, Adrian, was also deeply emotionally disturbed. His mother had been in hospital for most of his young life and he was totally bewildered, not certain to whom he belonged.

187

Jeanette was well aware that the two older boys had been witness to their mother's unbearable suffering during the summer before she was finally taken into the hospice. She was determined to help them regain their equilibrium, but Greg and Jeff steadfastly resisted all her attempts to show them that she and the Family really cared about them.

Not only was Jeanette now made the legal guardian of Amy's three boys, but she had become the legal mother of Sandra and Luke whose adoption had been finalised despite opposition from their mother. Julie had refused to sign the adoption papers. For one long harrowing day Sandra and Luke had to listen to the solicitors arguing the case in Court. Julie's objections had finally been outweighed by the fact that the children had lived with Jeanette for the past seven years and looked upon her as their Mum. Moreover, they left the Judge in no doubt that they wished to be legally adopted by her.

Sandra, now eleven years old, was proving to be a very gifted child. Her school reports indicated that she had special talents for creative writing and, in particular, for art. She was a happy, intelligent little girl, fastidious in her ways, and was doing her best to help and befriend the contemporary Susie. Her brother, Luke, had never fully recovered from the damage of those first years of abuse. He lacked co-ordination and was not physically strong enough to join in gym classes or outdoor ball games. But he had settled happily in a special school for the delicate where he coped very well. A dark-eyed, dark-haired, good looking little boy, he was a much-loved member of the Family. And everyone was delighted when his and Sandra's adoption was finalised.

Unfortunately, there was no longer any hope that Ted's adoption, or that of his brothers, Brian and Roger, would now go through. Despite the efforts of all the many people who tried to act as intermediaries between Jeanette and the adoption agency, they would have nothing more to do with her or the Family. Jeanette worried constantly whether the consequences for the Family, and in particular for Ted, were her fault. Perhaps if she had handled the staff of the agency more tactfully...? But she could not have kept quiet and ignored Ray's needs. She now accepted that even had she felt it politic to do so, she could not have acted against that principle.

Nigel Evans had selected the title for his film long before he became aware of the rift between Jeanette and the agency. Now, to his disbelief, they initiated proceedings to have the film stopped. He supposed that the reason for this extraordinary intervention must stem from the title; that the agency feared he was going to 'take the lid off' and expose their social workers' inadequacies. With no intention of succumbing to the pressure they were exerting, he went to see them and it was finally agreed that when the film was finished, he would give them a private showing, thus proving that the content did not refer in any way to them.

With so much preying on Jeanette's mind, she welcomed the timely advent of their move to Essex. She and Joyce had made several visits to the convent and had seen the old isolation hospital at the far end of the twenty-acre estate. The dwelling now housed nine men and women, each with their own bedroom and bathroom. The leprosy which had once afflicted them was no longer infectious, but their geographical isolation limited their social contacts.

The Old Convent had been left as it was when the nuns had vacated it several weeks previously. Ken Start had promised that the housing association would provide labour for the necessary repairs or alterations and there would be no lack of willing hands within the Family to effect their own decorations and improvements.

A week before the move, the Family went down to the convent to enable Jeanette and Joyce to see what needed doing and to measure windows for curtains and floors for carpets. They were totally unprepared for the reception they received from a member of the staff at St Giles, the old people's home. At first the woman refused to give them the keys to the little cabin where Lucy was to live, but when Jeanette insisted, she threw them on the ground at her feet. She made no effort to hide her hostility. The site manager from whom they obtained the keys to the convent was equally hostile. He had not been advised that they had permission to stay there and was clearly surprised to see them.

During that preliminary weekend visit to the convent Jeanette and Joyce were preoccupied by their encounter with two of the residents who walked over the intervening garden to welcome them. They were shocked to discover how institutionalised the two men were. They had to be instructed to go into the building and were pathetically grateful when they were told to sit down and were given a cup of coffee. Both men, one called Patrick, the other Neville, were nervous and confused. Both seemed to be very much in awe of the nurse, although she had looked after the old people for many years and was considered by the doctors who worked with her to be competent and capable.

Jeanette and Joyce returned to London very uneasily. Their reception so far did not reflect Ken Start's enthusiasm; moreover, the condition of the two St Giles residents they had met suggested a very different philosophy of care from their own. There was much that needed to be done, they thought, but they both welcomed the challenge.

Nigel filmed the day of their move from London, still hoping that the merging of the two communities would make a perfect ending to his documentary. It was only gradually, as one unfortunate event followed another, that they would all be forced to realise that the Family were very far from welcome.

Chapter 19

'Over 70% of the neglected children were aged less than 5 years with a mean age of 3 yrs 8 mths. There were more sexually abused children in the youngest age group... than in previous years. 14% of the sexually abused children were aged less than 5 yrs in 1985 compared to 4% in previous years.'
(Initial Findings, 1985, from NSPCC Register Research)

For the first fortnight, all seemed to go relatively well despite the unconcealed hostility of the nurse and the other members of staff. Jeanette and Joyce both felt that given time and the mutual will to develop their community as they had planned with Ken Start, the nurse's attitude would soften.

The children quickly made friends with the old people and Nigel filmed them together, both in St Giles, where two of the residents taught some of the boys to play snooker, and in the convent, where Sandra sat drawing an exceptionally good portrait of Mrs Cox, the elderly partially blind woman she had befriended. Five of the old people were frequent visitors to the convent and the children were in and out of St Giles. The quiet unsmiling Neville and the nonagenrian, Percy, could now be seen happily holding one of the Downs Syndrome twins on their laps. But this initial success did little to change the nurse's attitude.

Jeanette and Joyce soon realised that some of the old people were living in very real fear of the nurse. They considered that the meals given them were unimaginative and devoid of all luxuries. They were not permitted to go to the kitchen to make themselves a hot drink, although they did have a kettle in their television room. With total disregard for the associations it might have for these ex-lepers, a bell was rung to announce mealtimes, the arrival of the doctor or a visitor. If the residents disobeyed any of the rules, they were deprived of some privilege by the nurse and, Nigel was eventually to discover, were even hit by her.

Meanwhile she had aligned three of the residents and all the staff against the Family, thus dividing the community. Only five of the nine residents braved her wrath and continued associating with Jeanette and the children.

As trained nurses, Jeanette and Joyce realised that the old people were very institutionalised and depressed; but the nurse would not permit their interference. She objected to any attempt by them to do what they thought would improve the quality of life for the residents. Lucy, who was now cooking for them, was reprimanded when she tried to augment their menus. She did so nonetheless, knowing that she could give them far more interesting and nutritious meals on the budget permitted her.

Every morning, the site manager would arrive at the convent with a list of complaints: the children were walking on the grass, riding their bicycles on the paths, picking flowers, and someone was misusing the washing machines. It was decided that the Family could not continue to use the communal laundry facilities and must replace their own defunct washing machine. Since there was insufficient money for them to do this, they were having to do all the washing by hand in the bath.

Despite Jeanette's repeated requests for the provision of heating, she was told by the Springboard Housing Association that nothing could be done until the electricity sub-station was completed. Meanwhile several of the younger children became ill because of the cold, damp conditions.

Jeanette had never before been at a loss to think of ways to tackle the many problems she encountered. But now she was at her wits' end wondering how to rectify this increasingly fraught situation. The Springboard Administrative Officer came to talk to her. He was a kind, Christian caring man, but he seemed unable to comprehend what was happening, and had no idea how to go about uniting the two communities.

Joyce was completing the academic year at the college where she was tutoring, although she had handed in her resignation, and so was not on hand to support Jeanette when the children were blamed for offences which they had not committed. The children themselves were confused, for they too, had been expecting a happy united atmosphere. Moreover, they had become aware of the distressed state of some of the old people and some were frightened by the inexplicable undercurrent of violence.

They had every reason to be frightened. One night, not long after midnight, a car drove past the convent and a shot was fired, breaking the living-room window and showering the floor with glass. Jeanette called in the police, but although they came out to make enquiries, they reached the conclusion one of the children must have been responsible. They disregarded Jeanette's patient explanation that the shot had come from a passing car and that none of the children could drive, and moreover, it was well after midnight and they were all in bed.

As winter gave way to spring, Jeanette and Joyce grew daily more anxious about the situation. Maintenance men were coping with the repairs and alterations to the convent and the place was in chaos. No one was happy. The children were by now aware of the antipathy of some of the staff at St Giles and became more and more disinclined to go over there, knowing they would only receive rejection and criticism. These were all children who had, in one way or another, already suffered adult rejection in their lives, and because of it, they were perhaps more sensitive to rebuttal than other children might have been. Yet they knew most of the old people were pathetically grateful for their company and attention. Wendy had even managed to get one of the residents, who they had been told rarely spoke, to talk to her and not to hide behind trees and walls when she went to visit him. Through Lucy's efforts, the residents had also begun talking to each other in the Home and to sit chatting to one another after meals; at Jeanette's suggestion, they were using the dining-room as a communal place where they could enjoy each other's company. Several of them now started to accompany Jeanette and the children on shopping trips, despite the nurse's objections.

The situation deteriorated. The nurse banned Ray from St Giles, expressing her dislike of him in very strong terms. She accused Lucy of stealing and forced her, since she had been forbidden by Jeanette to retaliate, to hand in her resignation.

Matters became still worse. Some unknown person vandalised the old people's home, ripping the green baize of the snooker-table. The lining of the children's paddling pool was slashed. Cars outside the convent and St Giles had their tyres let down; windows were broken. Graffiti of a Satanic nature were scrawled over the walls of Lucy's cabin. When the police were called in to investigate, they were told that Lucy was mentally unbalanced and had probably damaged the cabin herself. Fearing that she was bringing trouble on the Family, Lucy thought seriously of going back to London; but Jeanette dissuaded her.

There had been three hundred pounds worth of damage done to the snooker-table, but the police could not find the culprit. The following morning, Jeanette discovered a huge painted message scrawled on the outside wall: GO BACK TO LONDON OR DIE. One of the little ones, playing in the garden, was almost hit by an air-gun pellet, which was later found lodged in Neville's wheelchair. All the windows at the back of the house were peppered with pellet holes. A chainsaw belonging to Springboard was stolen from the shed. Once again, the children were suspected of doing the damage and were subjected to questioning.

Nigel was concerned enough by now to contact his own lawyer and arranged for Neville to be visited by a solicitor. Jeanette was told that Neville, who had not been up to the convent for several days, was being kept a virtual prisoner in his room with no better explanation than that he had a bad foot and couldn't walk.

Ignoring the consequences, Jeanette and Nigel wheeled him back to the convent, but a member of staff called soon afterwards to say that if Neville was not returned to St Giles immediately, the Family would be in danger of eviction. Later that evening they took him back, only to be told next day by

Neville that on his return he had been struck by the infuriated nurse.

Ken Start at last came down to see Jeanette. As calmly as she could, Jeanette pointed out that he, of all people, should know that the offences that had been committed were uncharacteristic of her children. It was the behaviour of vindictive adults, she reiterated.

She told him of the effect this was having on the Family, not least upon Lucy who had made an enormous change for the better for the old people. More often than not, Lucy had returned to the convent sobbing because she had been verbally abused by the staff for interfering in the St Giles routine, yet the residents themselves, formerly so quiet and withdrawn, could now be seen smiling, helping with the cooking and cleaning. They could be heard singing, chatting to one another. It was if they had come alive after a living death under the old regime.

Many of the old people had confessed to Jeanette how lonely and forgotten they had once felt. Neville, in particular, had broken down and whilst Jeanette had held him like a child in her arms, talked tearfully of the years of isolation and fear he had lived through. Did Ken realise, she asked, that this needless cruelty was continuing?

Ken tried to placate Jeanette. The nurse had been in charge of the old people for a long time and they had adapted to her routine, he pointed out. It was understandable that she resented interference and was reacting to it.

'In a few years' time, it will all settle down and sort itself out!' he said. It was the only consolation he felt able to offer since he could see now that Jeanette's principles would never allow her to accept the nurse's rigid regime.

Bitterly, Jeanette reflected that by the time it had sorted out itself, ninety-year-old Percy would be dead, and that to allow what she felt was the needless suffering of the other residents to continue was a far cry from the Christian ethics behind the plan to unite the two factions. Moreover, she asked, did Ken not appreciate the effect this was having on the children? The police openly suspected them of being responsible for all the damage and since they had not been involved, they could not understand why they were being blamed.

Neither Jeanette nor Joyce knew when they first arrived that there were a great many others who objected to the Family coming to live at the convent. At St Giles, several of the old staff had been made redundant and since most lived in nearby villages, their loss of employment – and in one case their tied house – had caused a lot of local resentment. The nurse, in particular, had no intention of allowing her present regime at St Giles to be disrupted by the newcomers.

The decision by the Springboard Housing Association to take over the management of the St Giles estate and to work towards the two communities becoming spiritually and physically interwoven, had been an altruistic one. Unfortunately, however, the practical realities had not been fully explored by either the Association or Jeanette. There had been no prior liaison between the staff at St Giles and Jeanette, with their rôles spelled out and mutually agreed. No one had doubted that the arrangement would benefit everyone concerned and bring a new element of happiness and Christian unity into all their lives.

Local hostility had been further aroused before the Family had moved into the Convent, by an understandable – if unjustified – fear of the arrival of so many East End children in the area. A lot of people presumed that these children were trouble-makers, hooligans, out of control and likely to create havoc in their peaceful country village. No one had thought to explain to them that most had been deprived of parental care and love, and that many were in need of special understanding; that the 'crimes' that had been committed were *to* them and not *by* them; that the convent was not about to become a type of Borstal. No one appeared to realise that this was a family – albeit an unusually large one – *like any other*, and the site manager and his wife seemed to be under the misapprehension that this was a Children's Home; that Jeanette was employed by the Springboard Housing Association to run it; that he and his wife had been employed to supervise the running of the Home and ensure that the children were properly cared for. On one occasion his wife was discovered dressing the twins, Owen and Philip, having decided of her own accord that it would be beneficial to them if she took them out for a walk! Soon afterwards, a workman called to collect some of Jeanette's chairs, which he innocently believed were the property of the Association.

Jeanette was bewildered, dismayed and very angry. She attempted to explain that The Old Convent was *her* home, the children *her* children; that the furniture belonged to the Family, and that they had scrimped and saved to buy it. If the babies needed a walk, she said emphatically, *she* would arrange it. The site manager's wife, whose intentions had been for the best, was upset and allied herself with the members of the hospital staff who objected to the Family's sudden invasion.

Furthermore, Jeanette was nonplussed. Ken – this Christian friend of so many years standing who had devoted his life to helping others – was apparently unwilling to intervene on the Family's behalf. Was it possible, she now wondered, if he too thought the children guilty?

By now it was summer and, with an overwhelming feeling of relief, the Family left the convent for the untroubled atmosphere of Farleys for their holiday. Percy, Neville, blind Mrs Cox went with them, and three more residents joined them later. Everyone's spirits revived during that holiday. Neville smiled, talked again, and was even persuaded by Ted to feed one of the calves each day from a bucket. Old Percy sat in a deckchair watching the twins playing on the grass; Mrs Cox sat on a chair with her face turned to the sun, perfectly content despite her blindness, to enjoy the sound of the children's voices and laughter. Nigel was delighted with his filming as he captured their joy with his camera; yet the old people's delight in such simple pleasures highlighted the degree of their past deprivations.

Nigel did not share Jeanette's hope that someone from the Housing Association would bring about a reconciliation with the staff at St Giles, and he was apprehensive for the future.

His fears were well-founded. Jeanette was informed by telephone that in their absence, the cottage attached to the convent where beds were stored, had been vandalised. The beds had been dragged outside on the grass; the swimming pool had been slashed beyond repair; blood had been smeared on the walls of the washrooms. Unbelievably, it seemed the police still suspected that someone in the Family had perpetrated these

197

outrages. Patiently, Jeanette pointed out that the children were a hundred miles away and could not possibly be responsible. But the official attitude was that one or more of them could have got back to the convent!

'This is ridiculous!' said Jeanette, now very angry indeed. 'They have no transport – none of them can drive. The only way they could have got back would have meant a three-mile walk to the station, buying a train ticket to London – although they have no money; finding their way across London to Liverpool St Station, getting another train to Chelmsford and then finding a bus or walking the seven miles to the convent – and all this, together with the return journey, without detection. Besides, if any child here is missing for more than an hour, their absence would be noticed.'

This logical deduction that the children must be innocent was ignored.

'With so many children to keep an eye on, you can't account for their movements every minute of the day,' she was informed.

Jeanette realised now that logic, fact, the truth did not come into this situation. She could have argued that it was *because* her many children were very much under her control all the time that she was able to cope with them and their varied emotional problems. Nearly all her children were fostered and she was therefore answerable to the local authority for their care. For any one of them to be away without her knowledge for what could not be less than a period of eight hours was not simply improbable, but impossible.

'It is perfectly obvious,' she said bitterly to Joyce, 'that our kids are to be made the scapegoats for no better reason than that the police can't find the real culprits. Now just let them try to *prove* the kids guilty!'

There was worse to come.

When they returned to the convent, accompanied by a newly acquired goat, heifer and calf, they found a letter awaiting them from the Springboard Housing Association stating that, from now on, they must not cross the boundary between their garden and the grounds surrounding St Giles. The family were banned from entering the Home, and the stream was to form the demarcation line between the two properties. The Trustees of the St Giles Trust had written to Springboard saying they felt unable to guarantee the safety of the children, and that the children could be subject to violent attack if the association between the two communities continued.

Jeanette was close to heartbreak. Despite her request to Ken Start for an explanation, he appeared to take the line of least resistance.

In fact, Ken had reached the conclusion that no matter who was responsible for the shocking events taking place on the St Giles estate, the hostility could not be allowed to continue. He believed that both communities were suffering and that the relationship between them had gone beyond the point of reconciliation. The Springboard Housing Association did not own the lease of the convent and privately he feared that since Jeanette's family seemed to be under suspicion, the St Giles Trust might take the attitude that it would be best to terminate their lease of the convent, thus rendering them homeless.

The Chairman of the Trust later denied to Jeanette that there was ever a possibility of them being evicted, but Ken did not think it was in anyone's interest to allow the situation to deteriorate still further. He appreciated Jeanette's fierce resentment that her children should be under suspicion, but were he to have taken up cudgels on the Family's behalf, it could have meant a rift in the Association's good relations with the St Giles Trust. Springboard had over two thousand other families on their books to be considered. He had therefore endorsed the Association's letter to Jeanette requesting that the two communities be separated.

He himself did not appreciate that this letter might well condemn Jeanette's children in other people's eyes. Despite Jeanette's and Joyce's letter and telephone calls protesting that the decision could do no less than have that effect, he felt a meeting between all those concerned might only exacerbate the situation. This was something he was anxious to avoid as he greatly respected Jeanette's work with the children, and was personally fond of her and of them. He trusted that when she had had time to review the separation of the communities more calmly, she would see that it was the only logical method of putting an end to the conflict and allowing both the Family and the St Giles community to settle down in peace. He did not, therefore, go down to see her. The residents themselves had sent a petition instigated by Percy to the St. Giles Trust, requesting that the ban should not be enforced since, in effect, it meant that they could no longer invite their friends to their own home. This petition was ignored.

Totally unmaterialistic by nature as she was, Jeanette did not even then suspect why her former friend had apparently withdrawn his support. A less naive person might have surmised that the Springboard Housing Association was financed by the wealthy St Giles Trust and could not risk losing their patronage by backing Jeanette against their own employees. But no rational explanation had been given in that letter – nor person or persons likely to perpetrate the 'violent attack' identified.

It was clear from a letter Jeanette received from the Springboard Housing Association and signed by Ken that Lucy was being made the focal point for their complaints. The letter implied that Lucy's behaviour was autocratic and deliberately provocative.

It was true that Lucy's manner – in her determination to help and protect the old people – was often forceful and direct; and that she lacked the social experience which might have enabled her to handle the staff with all the necessary diplomacy. It was now obvious that her campaign to improve the residents' meals and dining-room facilities was being looked upon as a deliberate challenge to the staff. Lucy was bitterly upset.

In March, she was formally advised that Springboard were seeking a possession order for the cabin where she lived on the grounds that the accommodation was allocated for persons with 'special needs' and that Lucy no longer needed these 'special facilities'. No one could understand the wording of the possession notice since she had never required 'special facilities' and her tenancy of her flat in London had been a straightforward transfer to St Giles.

Lucy was by no means the only subject for Springboard's objections. Other members of Jeanette's family were accused in a letter of being physically and verbally abusive; of displaying 'unpleasant, violent and anti-social ways of behaviour'. In June, they received a letter from solicitors acting for Springboard, accusing members of the Family of harrassing the staff on the telephone; and warning Jeanette that if she could not 'restrain' her family, the question of their continued residence at the convent would have to be examined.

Jeanette was miserably aware that the events of the past few months were having a seriously demoralising and detrimental effect upon the older children. It was an impossibility – even had she wished to do so – to keep them out of the picture. They were all involved, although the younger ones and those whose understanding was limited, did not fully grasp the facts. Even they, however, were aware that Jeanette was upset and angry, and Neal whose nature, like that of all Down's Syndrome children, was intensely loving, now decided to do something about his Mum's distress.

He was not very clear as to the reasons for it, but he did understand that in part it had to do with the little stone footbridge crossing the stream that was the new demarcation line between their garden and the St Giles community. That they must *never cross the bridge* had been impressed upon them all. It now occurred to him that if he were to destroy it, the problems would be resolved and his Mum, Joyce and all the Family, would be happy again.

He went out late one evening with a hammer and began methodically to get rid of it. Jeanette, hearing strange knocking noises in the garden, went down to investigate. When Neal explained what he was doing and his reasons for it, she was close to tears. Patiently, she tried to explain to him that the destruction of the bridge would not achieve his aim in any way; that there was a perfectly good public road leading from the convent to St Giles and this could not be destroyed in order to keep the communities from seeing each other. The bridge was merely a symbol.

The boy seemed to grasp what she was trying to explain, but the following day, Jeanette was obliged to telephone the administrator and confess that this time it actually was one of the children who had vandalised the property and that she would of course pay for the damage. Fortunately, the administrator was very understanding and made no claim for repairs.

Ted, too, was reacting. Jewish by birth, he had come up against racial prejudice at school and at the Children's Home. He now reacted to what he saw as a campaign to get rid of the Family by sewing yellow stars on all the kid's clothing. His distress, however, was not comparable with the depth of Lucy's. One of the staff's gardens was vandalised. Lucy was promptly arrested by the local police. She was taken to the interrogation room and told that her past record was known to them; that she was a drug addict and that they were in no doubt she had perpetrated the damage. Fortunately, she had been in Jeanette's company at the time of the vandalism fetching the children from school and buying fencing for the adjoining field. She therefore had a water-tight alibi which obliged the police reluctantly to release her.

It seemed to the Family as if even the local police force was now aligned against them, and Lucy was convinced that because of her past reputation, *she* had brought all the trouble down on the Family's head. She became very distressed and spoke often of returning to London for the Family's sake. For five years she had led her life according to the Christian faith. Now it seemed that her former way of existence was to haunt her for ever; that she would never be fully accepted by other people.

Yet in a strange way, all these dreadful happenings drew the Family even closer together. The ban on the interchange of visits between the two communities and the total disregard for their petition had resulted in four of the old people moving in with the Family. There was nothing the Trustees could do to prevent this even had they so wished, since although St Giles was a charitable institution, the residents paid for their board and lodging with their own state allowances. They were free to go where they pleased.

The nurse was replaced by someone else but it was too late for any reconciliation. The ban was not to be lifted and Ken Start's consequent silence made it clear he was not prepared to intervene – even though the Springboard Housing Association had withdrawn their financial help. Jeanette had been informed that if she wished to remain at The Old Convent, she must be responsible for paying rent and costs amounting to £11,000 a year. The utter impossibility of meeting this demand – and in addition, the costs of rates, electricity and solid fuel – was causing her great anxiety. Moreover, she was now far from well. Although she would not give way to illness, she was permanently tired and often dispirited.

Joyce urged her to see a doctor but Jeanette refused. She was afraid she might have a malignant growth and that were she to seek medical advice, it would almost certainly mean hospitalisation. At that point in time she was not prepared to leave her family. Nor was she prepared even to consider leaving the convent. They would find the money for the rent somehow, she told Joyce. She was far more preoccupied by the prejudiced attitude of the local community towards her large family of East End children.

'Their reception, here and locally, has made a mockery of our kids' efforts not to give anyone cause for complaint!' Jeanette said bitterly. She minded – not so much for herself – as for her children.

'They may be well-mannered, fairly well-behaved and under control,' Joyce reasoned, 'but the locals don't know that, do they?'

Jeanette's greatest personal grief was the termination of her long-standing friendship with Ken Start. He had shared in their plans to bring happiness and comfort to the old people – in fact, he had initiated them. She could not understand why he seemed to lack the courage to vouch for the children's innocence. She was upset, too, for Joyce, who although she was now told the job of supervising the care of the old people at St Giles was still available, considered it would be totally illogical for her to cross the bridge to St Giles when she was part of the Family who had been banned from doing so.

But the necessities of day-to-day living did not permit long hours of regret or soul-searching for any of them. Even further demands on Jeanette's busy days were made by fresh calls upon her experience.

That October, she was asked if she would foster one or other of two brothers, Fred and Barry, aged nine and ten, who were beyond the care of the Children's Home.

It was now twelve years since she had agreed on impulse to take the two youngest of the Cook children, Gary and Ellen. At the time, she had not offered to take on their three elder sisters and she was appalled when she had recently learned that one was now a drug addict and the other two had been charged with soliciting. She had vowed then that no matter how many siblings were involved, she would never again refuse refuge to a needy child. She therefore agreed to take the two boys on the understanding that both would come together – and on a permanent basis.

Chapter 20

'... 300 *children in England and Wales are killed by their parents every year, about 3,000 receive serious injuries (including permanent brain damage) and another 40,000 are victims of assault...*'
(*Neil Frude,* Psychological Approaches to Child Abuse, *Batsford, 1980)*

A month later, as November drew to a close, Jeanette was asked to foster Vicky, another sexually abused child. When she went to collect Vicky from the Children's Home, taking some of her own children with her, they met Linda, another young girl who Jeanette realised was mentally handicapped. One of the staff related Linda's shocking history and as Jeanette listened to it, she made up her mind that if it could be arranged, she would foster this child as well as Vicky.

Linda had been 'In Care' almost from babyhood. She had been allowed to return to her parents at the age of seven on the understanding that her social worker visited her every week to ensure that her parents were not harming her. But the visits were not made, and it was three long months before a social worker called. Denied entry by the parents, he telephoned the police, who, unlike him, had the authority to demand entry into the house.

Linda was disovered on the floor of the lavatory with a fractured skull. The doctor who examined her thought the injury had been caused by a severe beating some weeks earlier. There was half a pint of pus on the seven-year-old child's brain, causing irreparable brain damage. There had been a plate of cat food on the floor and it was assumed that this had kept her alive and that she had drunk water from the lavatory bowl.

The little girl's injuries were so horrific that when the case came to Court, the Judge did not allow the photographs of her, taken when she was found, to be circulated to the jury. The father received a prison sentence, but it was too late to remedy the consequences for Linda. Once more 'In Care', and having made an astonishing physical recovery in hospital, she was sent to the Children's Home where Jeanette found her ten years later.

Jeanette felt immediate concern for the girl's future. In a year's time, Linda would be eighteen and could no longer remain in the Home. The children in the Family were also concerned. They plied Jeanette with questions.

'Why can't we have Linda as well as Vicky?'

'But what will happen to her, Mum, if we don't have her?'

'It'll be good for Sylvie to have someone the same as she is. You aren't just going to leave her there, are you, Mum?'

Sylvie was now twenty-three although she appeared much younger. She was also far less brain damaged than Linda. But Jeanette bowed to pressure from her children and from the house mother who had looked after Linda for so long in the Home. She did what she had wanted to do from the first – she arranged to foster Linda.

At this time Ray was giving Jeanette increased cause for concern. In the spring, he had stolen two hundred pounds of the housekeeping money before running away – and had spent it on clothes so that he could dress up as an American tourist. In the summer he had stolen Sandra's bike and again run away; when the police picked him up, he told them that he had stolen the bike from a shop, and added that he had broken into a Chinese take-away and stolen money from the till. He would tell any lie in order to draw attention to himself.

That Christmas he dressed up in women's clothes and made advances to his social worker. With her health rapidly deteriorating, Jeanette felt he must have proper psychiatric treatment. His social worker, shocked by his female attire and bizarre behaviour, agreed that he must be admitted to a residential Assessment centre. Although this meant that he would be under lock and key for three months, Jeanette accepted the plan, knowing that at least he would be safe. This was a child with problems and needs which required immediate specialised assessment. The only alternative to the residential centre was for him to treated by a local psychiatrist, but this would take time to arrange and the deteriorating state of her health would not allow for this unavoidable delay. Reluctantly Jeanette now realised that for the present she could do no more than reassure Ray that she cared; and that the Family's home was always there waiting for him.

Had she not been feeling so ill, Jeanette might have foreseen the repercussions of Ray's removal to the Assessment Centre. She only discovered after he had left that since she was no longer fostering him under her roof, the authorities no longer looked upon her as his foster mother; therefore, whilst his own mother had visiting rights, Jeanette could not see him. She had only succeeded in persuading Ray himself to accept the decision to remove him by giving him her word that she would visit him every Tuesday. She had a difficult fight, aided by Ray's social worker, to fulfil her promise.

Meanwhile, Joyce was growing steadily more concerned about Jeanette's condition. For a long time she had been in no doubt whatever that Jeanette had a growth. It was now so large that it had become apparent. She was also losing a great deal of blood. Without a biopsy it was impossible to know whether the growth was malignant and, over and over again, Joyce urged her friend to seek medical attention. Stubbornly, Jeanette equally often refused to do so.

Nigel Evans was one of the few people who was aware of the fact other than Joyce, and he realised that there was a possibility that Jeanette could die. The prospect of what would happen to the Family shocked and worried him. They had been living from day to day on a hope and a prayer that sufficient funds would turn up – to pay the bills. During one of their long talks in the course of the filming at Farleys, Jeanette had told him how dependent she was upon the support of friends, churches and people like Bill Henry and Tim Powell, who had so often over the years quite literally provisioned the Family from their Community foods project. Saving for the future had always been an impossibility in the light of the need to pay for today. Nigel decided he must try to do something to secure the children's future – if only financially. After consultations with Jeanette, he initiated the formation of a trust, of which he himself would be one of the trustees.

Family in Trust came into being shortly before the showing of his documentary *In The Name of Charity*, which combined both earlier and later films. The sensitive and emotive nature of Nigel's documentary reached many people: donations were sent in by viewers, and the Family acquired eight hundred new friends who would regularly receive copies of the newsletter they had decided to distribute.

One man, Michael Miskin, and his wife were so moved by *In The Name of Charity* that they promptly asked Nigel for seventy cassettes of the film. Michael Miskin distributed these amongst his many business contacts, inviting their contributions. As a result of his personal involvement, the sum of thirty thousand pounds was raised for Family in Trust. His philanthropy went further than a single gesture; he also became a trustee and continued to devote much of his valuable time to raising further funds.

With the immediate worry of how to find the rent for the convent for the next two years resolved, Jeanette at long last went to see a doctor. Unable to understand how she could have delayed so long, he confirmed that she had a growth which must be removed immediately. It was now June and having won her fight to visit Ray, she kept her appointment at the hospital.

'And about time too!' Joyce said as she drove her there. 'You're stupid, pig-headed and selfish not to have gone before. We've all been worried about you. All the children have remarked how ill you look and some of them are convinced you're going to die! So take this opportunity to have a good rest.'

Jeanette's 'good rest' lasted for two days. A blood test taken prior to her operation showed that she was alarmingly anaemic. She was forthwith given four pints of blood – the doctor telling her that she really needed more – and was sent home for a month, after which time it was hoped she would be physically fit enough to face the operation. As gently as he could, the doctor told her that she had left her visit to him far too late and that the growth was now too big to be removed without a total hysterectomy.

It was far from being an easy month for Jeanette. She tried not to think about the future and instead reflected on the past year. Difficult though life had been, there had been compensations. It had once been thought that the little 'wolf boy', Jasper, would never walk or talk. Now, although he did not carry on a conversation, he could formulate the right words for all the familiar objects. During his psychology tests, which were many, he had done the puzzles so often that he could do them now without any effort. If he went to the kitchen to demand a 'drink' and nobody gave it to him, he would get it for himself, and seldom went without anything he wanted!

Jeanette knew he could never be entirely normal, but he was progressing well at his special school in Walthamstow. Physically he was a very active child. Jeanette had always to ensure that one of the other children were with him. Ben, who had now changed his surname to Roberts by Deed Poll, was particularly good with him. Jasper's behaviour was often that of a child of four although he had now had his eleventh birthday; but the psychologist had explained that any child must go through every stage of development. Not long since, Jasper had outgrown the inclination to smear his faeces on the walls – the five-year-old twins, Owen and Philip, were currently in this phase.

Everyone took turns to clear up after the children, and to care for the old people. Ninety-year-old Percy had had a bad bout of pneumonia that winter, and only their careful nursing had helped him to pull through. He was very frail, but a completely integrated member of the Family, as were Neville, Michael and blind Mrs Cox. Michael, with Jeanette's encouragement, was planning a visit to his native country, Cyprus, where he hoped to be reconciled with his wife who still lived there.

There were other many blessings for which she thanked God. Slowly, the Family was being accepted by the local community. The children were making friends at school and with their neighbours' children. The parents allowed their children to come to play and returned the invitations. The Family had built

209

an adventure playground in one of the adjoining fields and someone had presented them with old tyres for swings. A farmer had given them an old tractor to play on and the milkman had produced a defunct milkfloat which they could pretend to drive. They had even been given two old horses which were in need of a good home.

The new attitude to the Family – doubtless helped by the showing on television of Nigel Evans' documentary – was perhaps most apparent in the trust shown by neighbours when they employed some of Jeanette's older girls as baby-sitters.

Inevitably, there were still difficulties. Many of the teachers in the older children's schools were unused to handling children with the emotional problems of the abused. It was far from easy for Jeanette to rectify the distorted attitudes to parenthood and sex held by so many of her abused children, and vitally necessary that she should do so before they reached the age of maturity and adopted attitudes and modes of behaviour which would ultimately affect their children. Several years previously a lesbian teacher in Natalie's school had written 'Old-fashioned rubbish' on the child's essay on sex and marriage. The girl had expressed the views Jeanette had encouraged her to hold – that sex belonged rightfully within marriage between a man and a woman.

Natalie had been hopelessly confused by the teacher's remark. Only Jeanette's intervention with the headmistress had elicited an apology and a clear statement that the teacher had been wrong. The episode had highlighted Jeanette's belief that ordinary people in authority lacked the knowledge and understanding of so many of the problems relating to children like hers. It was not as if there were so few emotionally disturbed children with these problems. All teachers should, she believed, be made far more aware of this problem.

Often such children reacted violently against any physical contact by an adult. One of the fostered girls, determined to be part of the Family by adopting the surname Roberts, was called by her birthname; another was told that members of the family were not true 'brothers' or 'sisters'. These minor hiccoughs were off-set by their satisfaction in being treated as perfectly normal children and not as East End hooligans! One of the local schools, the Church of England Primary School, had never

210

failed to be co-operative and had made the children welcome from the start; they continued this good relationship.

Other good relationships were being formed. The home tutors who came to teach those children unable to go to school were sympathetic and competent. The decorating of the house by the older children was steadily progressing and The Old Convent now seemed very much like home. Although the heating had still not been installed, the better weather made it unnecessary for the time being. The swimming pool was in use again; the children had acquired pets – rabbits, goats, a dog, a tropical fish tank, cage birds.

It was a happy home despite the rifts with Ken Start and the adoption agency, and the enforced separation of the Family from the St. Giles community. There were many weekends and holidays when the grown-up children with their wives, husbands, children, came down to stay. Jeanette now had six grandchildren. There was, she realised, a great deal to be thankful for and she wished very much that she felt fitter to enjoy her blessings more fully.

By July, with Ray still in safe-keeping, Jeanette was more relaxed, but a few days before she was due to go back to hospital for her operation, she heard through a social worker about a ten-year-old boy in trouble. It was almost certain that at the case conference on his future then pending, the decision would be reached to despatch him to a locked unit. He ran away continuously from the Children's Home and, despite his age, the locked unit seemed the only alternative – other than Jeanette. But Jeanette had been told she must remain in hospital for at least two weeks and now she learned that the case conference was to be held during that period. Knowing that the impending operation and the state of her health might prejudice her chances of 'rescuing' this small boy, Jeanette told no one how ill she was.

Unaware of the reasons why she could not attend the case conference, the boy's social worker put forward Jeanette's offer to foster him, but as Jeanette drifted into unconsciousness under the anaesthetic, she was still worrying that she herself could not be present to insist that any alternative was better than locking up a boy of ten for the rest of his childhood.

On the day of Jeanette's operation, Percy died. Joyce and

211

Lucy were with him, holding his hands, and he died very peacefully. Nevertheless he had become a much loved and respected member of the Family and now they all grieved for him. Jeanette, who was supposed to remain in hospital for two weeks, discharged herself after seven days. She was determined that she would attend Percy's funeral, which had been delayed so that she could be there, whatever the cost to her health.

In the eighteen months that she had known him, she had come to love and respect the charming and intelligent nonagenarian. He had become her friend and ally, always ready with his astonishing intellect to advise and support her, yet equally ready to play chess with Ben or nurse one of the twins. They were all going to miss him.

Jeanette did not go back into hospital, although a number of her abdominal stitches had broken during Percy's funeral. Still very weak, she sat in the garden on a hot sunny day, the younger children continually running to her with their childish requests. 'Mum, can I ride Jeff's bike?' 'Mum, can I feed the rabbits?' Little Adrian was playing with the twins, Owen and Philip, on the slide. Jeanette's thoughts were only partially with them. She was to take on the ten-year-old newcomer three days hence and knew from experience that the period after a child's arrival was always very demanding of her time and attention.

This particular boy, she had been told, was so violent that not only the other children in the Home but the staff too, were frightened of him. Jeanette smiled to herself, knowing that she had heard this same story many times before.

Three days later, she was fit enough to take a slow walk round the garden. From behind the shrubbery, a figure suddenly appeared. It was the new boy who had introduced himself as 'Jack the Lad'. In fact, he was a small, sturdy, good-looking youngster with a mop of light brown hair. The colour of his brown eyes was difficult to see as he screwd them up in a scowl that matched the determined upward tilt of his jaw.

It had not taken Jeanette long to realise that his aggressive, challenging manner was his way of covering up a desperate insecurity. But now, for a moment, she was startled out of her complacency. The boy was holding a garden fork and pointing it at her.

212

'That's dangerous,' she said in her quiet voice. 'Put it down!'

Other members of the Family could have told him that when Jeanette used that particular tone, there was little point in argument. But Jack the Lad was new.

'Just fucking make me!' he said, jabbing the garden fork closer to her. 'Nobody messes with me – see?'

'Put it down!' Jeanette repeated.

For a moment, silence reigned. Jeanette felt a twinge of anxiety. She was still very weak and if it came to the point where she must physically remove the fork from him, she was far from sure she could do it. But she gave no indication of her doubts. The boy too, was unsure. His hesitation gave Jeanette the clue she needed. She drew a deep sigh.

'Look, I'm much too busy to hang about here,' she said. 'So if you're going to stick that thing in me, hurry up and do it.'

The garden fork was lowered, so fractionally that Jeanette was not sure if she had really seen a movement. Then the child's scowl deepened as he shrugged his shoulders with an attempt at nonchalence.

'I'll stick you when *I'm* good 'n ready – not when *you* tell me, see?'

He thrust the fork into the ground where it stood between them.

'Right!' said Jeanette cheerfully. She pulled it out of the ground and leant it against a tree. 'Let's get back to the house, shall we? It must be nearly tea-time.'

She reached out her hand and ruffled his hair. The scowl disappeared. Tears were not far off – but Jack the Lad squared his shoulders.

Some of the older children were returning from school and Jeanette could hear their voices as they called out to the little ones. There was the hint of a smile at the corners of her mouth. Was it happiness at this first small victory? Jack the Lad did not see it as Jeanette put an arm lightly round his shoulders.

The middle-aged woman and the little boy walked side by side towards the house. Anyone who saw them might easily have mistaken them for a very ordinary mother returning home with her son.

THE END

213

The Family in 1987

JEANETTE has now fully recovered her health. Since the summer of 1986, she has incorporated four more children into the Family. Her faith in the future remains unchanged, as does her determination to fight for her children's rights whenever she feels they are in jeopardy. Jeanette's tolerance with her children is unlimited, and she is still trying with Joyce's help to become more tolerant of bureaucratic bungling – but her heart is not really in it!

She remains devoted to Betsy and her children who she sees frequently, as she does Dan and his family.

Discussions are taking place, but for the present no agreement has been reached to secure a long-term licence for Jeanette and the Family to continue living at The Old Convent.

She now has seven grandchildren.

JOYCE now shares responsibility for the Family with Jeanette on a full-time basis. She is chauffeur, secretary, organiser as well as 'aunt' to all the children, and frequently gives talks or lectures when Jeanette is too busy to do so herself. Her former experience as a District Nursing Tutor is proving very useful on such occasions. She remains a devoted member of her own family who are frequent visitors to the convent.

She continues to provide Jeanette with unending moral and practical support. She is not only Jeanette's loyal, dependable friend; her fundamentally pragmatic nature and cheerful, logical approach to life enable her perfectly to complement Jeanette.

ROBBIE is now out of the army and has a full-time job as a bus driver. He is the proud father of a baby boy whose surname is registered as 'Roberts' – the first of Jeanette's grandchildren to be so called. He and his family are frequent visitors and he remains in close touch with the Family.

JOAN and LARRY have recently celebrated their eighth wedding anniversary. They have two boys aged seven and four who often telephone Jeanette. They live in London and stay with the Family at weekends as often as they can.

CATHY has two children by her first marriage and is now contemplating a second marriage. She and her children visit when they can and she telephones frequently. The problems she had in the past relating to Wendy no longer exist.

TOM is employed as a Care Attendant in residential homes for the elderly and mentally handicapped. He stays in touch with one of his army cadet officers who is now a friend of the Family. From time to time, Tom takes his friends to visit Jeanette, and he is always in telephonic touch with the Family. He is thinking of joining the army.

GARY and ELLEN were adopted in December of 1986. Both are studying for their O-levels and both have applied to join the police force. Gary has meanwhile obtained a job with a local builder. He attends the church youth club and also weightlifting classes. Ellen is interested in hairdressing and pottery. They are very average teenagers with the usual adolescent joys and problems. They both enjoy school.

NATALIE has now been reconciled with her husband, Tim, after a stormy start to their marriage. During the course of two six-month periods of separation, Natalie returned to the Family but she, Tim and their two-year-old daughter, Wendy, hope now to have a stable family life of their own.

SANDRA is now in the third year of her secondary school. She takes a particular interest in art and in writing. An intelligent, pretty girl, Sandra has many boy-friends whose phone calls frequently monopolise Jeanette's line! She plays basketball for her school, enjoys drama and her piano lessons, and is popular with the families of her friends. At home, she can be difficult, like any fourteen-year-old, but everyone loves her. She is a member of the church youth club.

LUKE is in a school for children with special needs where he is developing well. He gets on happily with his peers, but he still has difficulty relating to adults he does not know. He rides a motorbike, is eager to learn to drive a car and is anxious to learn to play the drums. He is not quite so anxious to have the obligatory piano lessons!

MICK shares a flat with any one of his many friends who he introduces to the Family whenever he visits them. Cheerful, good natured and always good company, he can and does turn his hand to many different jobs... driving, running a market stall, merchanting scrap. He likes always to be self-employed and is entirely self-sufficient.

SIMON attended college where he studied for a Social Science degree and Community Studies certificate. He now lives in London where he is involved in community work.

CATRINA returned to live with the Family last year and in December gave birth to a baby daughter. She is hoping to obtain a flat in the neighbourhood so that she can live near the Family. She has held jobs as a clerical worker in a school and a hospital records department, and worked as a Care Assistant in an old people's home. She is hoping for a job connected with graphic design or furniture restoring.

WENDY is at senior school where she is progressing well despite continuing problems with her health. She attends the St. John's Ambulance Brigade where she particularly enjoys the 'nursing' tasks, and she is a girl guide. She is friendly with many of the neighbours' children, particularly those who, like herself, are keen on horses and riding.

MARTIN was unhappy living alone in a flat in London where

216

he worked in a bank. He is now back home where he is a quiet, but very helpful, member of the Family. He still keeps his London flat and visits it sometimes, but he is hoping to find local accommodation. He keeps in touch with his natural brothers.

SYLVIE helps with all kinds of domestic work and with the little ones. She is a member of the local MENCAP Club and Drama Club. She is still in need of supervision but is continuing to develop skills in reaching her full potential and relates easily and happily to all age-groups.

JASON has made big strides emotionally although he is still a little behind his peers. He lives at home where he is particularly interested in all the animals and in gardening. His hobby is taxidermy. He belongs to the local church youth club. He has obtained a job as assistant maintenance man with a local council.

JASPER missed nine months of his schooling in Walthamstow due to transportation difficulties. Happily, these have now been resolved and he is responding well to his teachers, who are pleased with his progress. At home he is still hyperactive and in need of supervision, but he is a happy child.

LUCY: Unfortunately, the incidents that occurred at The Old Convent had a detrimental effect upon Lucy. She lost confidence in herself and her belief in the future was undermined. The Family are still trying to reassure her of her own value and to help her to regain her self-respect.

CLARE has obtained a local job as a nursing auxiliary, which she very much enjoys. She is currently considering undertaking nursing training. Meanwhile, she is learning to drive and already rides a Moped to and from work. She is a member of the local church youth club.

NEAL works hard around the house and garden to the extent of his capabilities. He will cheerfully tackle such jobs as window cleaning, floor scrubbing, washing up, and is a willing assistant to his brother, Ben, when fixing wall-tiles and carrying out other such DIY tasks. He is a member of the local MENCAP Club, which he attends every week.

BEN is still not relegated to a wheelchair although the deterioration of his muscles continues to take its course. He is extremely able with repairs around the house and supervises the heavier work he cannot do himself. He is realistic about his state of health but is nearly always cheerful and despite the extra physical effort it demands, will bravely undertake anything, such as a trip abroad or a day's trout fishing. His courage commands everyone's respect.

TED has left school and is enjoying his job in a supermarket. He is emotionally far more stable and is an active member of the youth club. He enjoys cycling.

BRIAN is at a school for children with special needs. He attends a day release college to do a link course. Recently, there have been no complaints from his school about his social behaviour and for months on end he behaves well at home. He is no longer dependent upon his brothers and gets on well with his contemporaries. He attends the local MENCAP Club.

ROGER is at the local comprehensive school where he has many friends. He is a strong, healthy, outgoing boy who is always cheerful and happily invites his friends home. His sunny nature ensures his popularity with everyone. He enjoys all kinds of sports.

OWEN and PHILIP were adopted by Jeanette in December last year. Both are walking, talking and are toilet-trained. Owen is physically the stronger of the twins, Philip more limited in his speech. They attend a special school where both are very active. The whole family are devoted to them and have to make concerted efforts not to spoil them!

RAY is in a residential therapeutic community boarding-school but returns home every third weekend. He still has many problems, is confused and manipulative, and he still runs away. The school is attempting to teach him to discipline himself so that he will be better able to cope with life when he reaches the age of eighteen.

GREG has a flat in the Midlands and has applied to go to college to study for a B.A. in English. He has three A-levels. He spends a great deal of his time writing stories. He is kind, gentle, caring and very good with the younger children. He stays in close touch with the Family and visits at weekends.

JEFF is catching up fast with his peers at the local comprehensive school where he is very popular. He wants to go to agricultural college where he can satisfy his great love for animals. He is a hard worker and very responsible. He is a member of the church youth club and attends the St. John's Ambulance classes. He plays football for the church team.

ADRIAN started school in January and is enjoying it. He is an intelligent, talkative, highly active little boy, affectionate and mischievous. He loves cooking and riding his bike.

SUSIE keeps up with her peers at the local comprehensive, although, having missed so much schooling, she requires special help. She likes to receive a lot of attention at home, but has settled down very well and is a happy child. She is concerned at the present about her little brother, who is in a Children's Home, and she would like him to join the Family.

FRED is doing a second final year in junior school to give him time to prepare for secondary school. He has not entirely recovered from a road accident in which he was injured prior to his arrival with the Family, and he has to take pills to minimise the risk of fits. He has settled down and he is a happy member of the Family although still wary of adults and mistrustful of any affection shown to him. He plays football for the school team and takes part in all the various activities.

BARRY is in his last year in junior school. He is an outgoing child, very protective of little Adrian. He needs extra help with his lessons. A physically active boy, he takes part in all the school activities and is going on holiday with them this summer.

VICKY has a home tutor who has become a friend of the family. Under her tuition, Vicky has developed a keen ability for art, craft work and sewing, and has made progress with her schoolwork. She helps to look after the younger children and old Mrs Cox, who is very attached to her. Vicky's sense of humour is one of her most likeable assets. She attends the St John's Ambulance classes.

LINDA can undertake some household tasks under supervision and she likes to help with the little ones. She is a member of the Girls Brigade and of the MENCAP Club.

JACK-the-LAD was found to have minimal brain damage following an E.E.G. It was recommended he should have home tuition. Although he still has temper tantrums, he now hits objects rather than people! He has a great sense of humour and an endearing personality and has settled down very well. So far, he has shown no inclination to run away!

MRS COX had her daughter from America to stay for three months as a guest of Jeanette's. The old lady remains in her own room most of the time although she joins the Family for parties. Her partial blindness has not deteriorated. The Family take it in turns to look after her.

NEVILLE went to hospital during the late summer of 1986 for an operation on one of his feet. He is now back with the Family amongst whose members he potters around during the day. He is particularly fond of the little ones and the animals. He attends the local MENCAP Club and Drama Club and also a club for the physically handicapped.

MICHAEL went to Cyprus on a three month return ticket, to meet with his wife, children and grandchildren after a gap of twenty years. He is back at the convent prior to rejoining his family in the summer on a permanent basis.

FOUR NEW ADDITIONS to the family are settling in – a twenty-year-old epileptic girl; a ten-year-old boy whose fostering broke down; a sixteen-year-old girl; and a baby of fifteen months who is temporarily with the Family on a Place-of-Safety Order.

Appendix 1 – 'My Mum' by her children

when i met seavelle Roberts i was about 12 to 14 i lived with her up to the age of 18 since then i have Been Married and had two children and Been Divorce. She has always Been There when i have Needed advice AND Help even Though she has Now 22 children to Look after
She is a mum in a million
and I would Do ANything for Her.

— Cathy ——————————————————

My Mum is My shepard. She leads Me through the bad times and shares the good. She loves me when she's angry, she loves me when she's glad. I'm proud of my mum, she does such good, helping kids less fortunate than most. Papers have said my muver is a Supermum, but I reckon she is a super dooper mum. There's no one else anywhere like my mum, and never will be, she's a mum in a million. If it were not for her I would proberly be in a chidrens home in Tower Hamlets. Mum has told me stories of when she first saw me, saying I was a beautiful kid and that. See wanted me to stay and live with her unfortunaty my birth mum caused complications, but my mum still had hope that eventoally I was to be her daughter for ever and ten years on here I am adopted and very happy. Theres no stopping her she'll foster kids till she drops because she is one of the few who care, I'm just happy she cared for me. Theres no where else i would rather be than by my mums side

— Sandra ——————————————————

What I think of my mum

I Love my mum for looking after me
and Feeding me I never get bord because
I have a lot to do.
my mum buys me alot of nice thing
clobhes and shoes.
I Love my brothers and sisters as well
and I Love my aunt Joyce.

— Barry ————————————————

I love mum because
I love mum because

she loves me.
She does me

— Adrian ————————————————

I feel mum is special.
I don't know where my life would
be without her.

To Mum. Thanks for putting up
with me these past fourteen years.
with love

— Ellen ————————————————

What Mum means to Me   L Michael

Mum means the Whole world
to me. Becaus she lets me go
to the park and Lets me Ride
me hours and play with all my
Brothers and sisters in the
Swimming pool and I play Foot-
Ball at home and at school we
play on our BMX's on the
track and She lets me go and
play in the snow and she means
everything to me.

— Fred ────────────────────

Muvver is a real gem, I
love her. I Know I can
Share the BAD times as well
as The good times. I know
that no-ather how much I hurt
her she will Still love me.
She has a Great sense of
humor and she cracks me
up.

— Ben ─────────────────────

I love mum lots.

— Neal ────────────────────

Mum means a lot to me
because she has help
me to start a new life
and mixx with othe
People and ~~sta~~ & she
has loved and cared for
me. She also taught me
what life is about she
is the best mum and
will be with me for ever
I have found love in her
naw I now wot love &
careing is she is the
beat mum Love

— Susie

what I think of my mum
I think my mum is the best mum in
the world because she looks
after me a lot and cares about
me a lot to. The same as evey
one else. The best bit about
mum is she is quite tall and I
like her smile too. but I dont
like her wen shes angrey but I
like her wen she smiles and is
happy too.

— Jack

Mum is kind to me She helps me
with my problems mum means a lot to me
If I was not with mum I would not be any thing
or do anything

— *Sylvie* —————————————————————

About thirteen years ago I was in a children's
home when I first saw Jeanette Roberts. I was standing
on the banister peeping throw the gaps of the stairs
and from that moment on my life changed.
I began to understand what love was and to be
loved. Over the thirteen years the love has grown as
my family has grown. My Mum Jeanette gave me a
happy and wonderful life which is special to each
of us.
New I am married I'd like to give my family the
kind of love that I was given. With Jeanette as my
Mother, Joyce as my Aunt and a wonderfully large
family what more could I ask for.

— *Natalie* —————————————————————

There is no one else like my mum.
Mum means the world to me. I probely
would not be alive today if it
were not for her love for me.
she showed me that I was needed
and not just another homeless
and parentless kid. And I really
love my mum even when I am in a
temper with mum. no one will replace
my lovely lovely mum xx

— *Luke* —————————————————————

I think mum is nice, because she
cares about people.
      mum shows me where I go wrong
so I can sort it out with her help

— *Debbie* —————————————————————

Begase I lived with Mum I was angry about my experience of life. But aer the years she has taught me this experience can be used to help others, living with her is the best thing that ever happened to me.

— Ted

I think my mum is a very special person. She has helped me through very difficult times and has always been there when I need her

It doesn't matter what I've done, I know she still loves me and I love her

— Catrina

Mum has taught me to realize that I'm not going to be alone in life She has also helped me to cope in different aspects of life. She is very patient and will help me and others in difficult situations.

— Jason

After being with mum for 14 years
I have become very attached to the
family. She has helped me in all
my problems. People may think that they
can just walk into the house and
all their problems are cured, but this is
not the case. Mum has to work very
hard to help everyone of us and it
does not take just a few day's. After
being in this family for this long Mum
still has to help me with my problems.
In fact as far as I'm concerned Mum
is fantastic, wonderful, excellent and
Brilliant.!!

— Gary ————————————————

mum has halPeoL ma
to care abovt otnars
shacares abovt ma
Love ner

— Brian ————————————————

Mum my mum

I think mum is a very nice mum because ~~I~~ She helps us with our problems~~,~~ and she look after ▮ us a lot

— Wendy

My Mum

The Only Way I Can describe My Mum is that I think ~~She~~ is the Best foster Mother any foster Child Like My Self Can have. and I love her Very Much

One day I'm going to foster her. And took after her and love her as She has me. When She's 90 that's When I know to buy her a Stop Sign... Until then She has all her grand-children that have to grow up too. and they Will love her too as much as we do my two boys love their Nan to pieces. Like I do and him? (my Husband

— Joan

My mum means everything to me. She does everything a normal mother does and a lot of things a mother can't do.
E.g We have a homemade BMX track and adventure play ground just across the road and my mum with help from the family desinged it and built it. We even have a death slide to play on. We also have two swimming pods which we use in the summer.

— Roger

Jeanette to me is a mum in a million, to whom i am gratful and Love.
and was Loved by.
I am a proud son of her's.
to see what she has done for me and so many other children Like me.

I will love her always.

— Robbie

I think my mum is caring, understanding and she is a wonderful mum. She means a lot to me.

— Clare

Mum means to me more than anything
else. In the Whole wide world
In the time that I have been with mum
she has helped more kids than I can
remember as well as bringing the family
together with her love. For us all.
Nothing so big, small, tall, wide can show
how great she is. And how great mum
she is to us all

— Jeff

What Mum means to me

Maureen
Age 16½.

Mum means a lot to me,

She has made me feel much

Better inside Since i came to

Live with her. I am now happy

i see life is worth something mum

made me see this. She helped

me with school work and I

Thank her for that and thankher

for Being Mum

— Vicky

I think mum is a very nice lady. I care
a lot about her. She helps me she get what
I need. She looks after me really well and I
love you mum.

— Linda

Befor I knew Mum (if I) I did not know what the word commitment meant.

I have watched her work with Children who are mentally handicapped, physically handicapped emotionally disturbed and children who have been sexually abused. When she makes a commitment to a child I have come to learn that means from that moment on she will show them a depth of caring that will mean they are no longer isolated. Through her they will learn that they are valuble human beings who, because of thier hurt have a lot... to give to other people. She gives them back thier self respect.

I have seen children hurt her again and again and I know that whatever each one of them does her relationship will still be there to support them. I have seen children who have been sexually abused bought to Mum for councilling some immediatly after they have been assulted and some years after they have been hurt. I have watched these children after Mum has conceled them and the relief of thier emotional pain has often left me feeling that if I could just help one person like that I would not have suffered for nothing.

Through Mum I have also come to realise how vitaly important it is that children who have been sexually abused should be given the opportunity of councilling with someone of who has Mums depth of understanding and perswerence. I have had the privilage of watching children heal through this lady. I remember once someone describing her as a gentle Giant.

— Lucy

Appendix 2 – What You Can Do To Help

ANY OF THE FOLLOWING ORGANISATIONS WILL WELCOME YOUR HELP

CHILDREN'S COUNTRY HOLIDAY FUND: If you live in the country or near the seaside and can offer a holiday to an underprivileged child from one of the deprived areas of London, please contact:

Children's Country Holiday Fund, 1 York St, London W.1. Tel: 01.218.4830 for further details. They will welcome your offer.

Your local Social Services Department, and the WRVS welcome offers of holiday accommodation; and your Citizens' Advice Bureau will notify you of your nearest Children's Country Holiday organisation.

DR BARNARDO'S: Dr Barnardo's is always in need of volunteers to assist with its work with children and families. They need flag-day collectors, child care visitors, mini-van drivers. They need people to befriend teenagers in trouble, to sell goods and cards provided through Barnardo's catalogues; to help in their gift shops. A regular commitment to help is invaluable to them, whether it be for half a day a week helping in a shop, a couple of hours once every few months shaking a tin outside a supermarket, or a fortnight once a year to help at a handicapped children's play scheme. Everyone's contribution is valuable.

You can:
(1) send for information about help needed in your area
(2) ask for details about local helpers' groups

(3) ask for general information leaflets giving an overview of the work of the organisation

Without the help from volunteers Barnardo's would not be able to run the many holiday activities they organise for mentally handicapped children or severely disadvantaged children living in inner cities or on large, run-down and isolated housing estates.

If you wish to offer your services as a volunteer contact:

Mr Elwyn Owens, Divisional Director, Dr Barnardo's, Tanners Lane, Barkingside, Ilford, Essex, IG6 1QG. Tel: 01.550.8822.

FAMILY NETWORK: Family Network require:

(1) volunteers who will talk to mothers under stress who need to air their fears and household problems

(2) part-time paid workers who will look after a handicapped child for an hour or two, in order to relieve the mother

(3) part-time paid workers who will babysit for couples whose marraige is at risk and who need a break

(4) part-time unemployed people to enrol through the Manpower Services Commission who will visit mothers in their homes and give them time to rest by taking the children out, playing with them, etc, to avoid stress arising

Male volunteers are urgently required, and, in particular, to present a father-figure to difficult children in one-parent families.

Family Network, The Methodist Chuch, Ilford Lane, Ilford, IG12JZ. Tel: 01.514.5444.

HOME-START VOLUNTEERS: Home-Start has over sixty schemes operating in this country offering support, friendship and practical help to young families experiencing difficulties, who are referred mainly by Social Workers and Health Visitors. Home-Start require volunteers who do not need academic or professional qualifications, but must normally be parents themselves and be prepared to undertake an initial course of preparation. This could mean one day a week for ten weeks, or evenings or at weekends.

Further information is obtainable from:
Margaret Harrison, Home-Start Consultancy, 140 New Walk, Leicester. Tel: 0533.554988.

NATIONAL FOSTER CARE ASSOCIATION: If you feel you could foster a child, even on a temporary basis, and would like further details as to what would be involved, please send a stamped addressed envelope to:
NFCA, Francis House, Francis Street, London SW1P 1DE. Tel: 01.829.6266/7, or:
NFCA, Volunteer Centre, 25/27 Elmbank Street, Glasgow, G2 4PB. Tel: Glasgow 041 226.
Fostering could mean caring for a child whose parent has had to go into hospital; a child who is at risk of abuse by its parents and is in need of a temporary home prior to a more permanent fostering; a child who needs permanent fostering because it cannot be returned to its natural parents; a child who is in danger of becoming institutionalised after a long spell in a Children's Home; a physically or mentally handicapped child who has failed to find a family to adopt it.
The 1986 fostering allowance, which varies from county to county, is between £19.50 and £75 per week depending upon the age of the child. The qualifications needed by a foster parent are not professional or academic, but require love and understanding of children and their needs. There is a desperate shortage of such proxy parents who are needed for the hundreds of children who have to be taken into Care.

NSPCC: The NSPCC does not use volunteers for their work with children who have been abused or neglected, but the Society's Appeals Division relies on the goodwill of volunteers to help raise the funds which are essential to helping children and families. The NSPCC have local committees and groups who are closely involved in their work and help coordinate and organise local-fund raising events. If you would like to volunteer your help, please contact:
Mr Robert Hardy, Appeals Division, NSPCC, 67 Saffron Hill, London EC1N 8RS.

PARENTS ANONYMOUS (LONDON): Parents Anonymous require volunteers

(1) to listen to the problems of parents in trouble (further details of this service can be obtained from Parents Anonymous)

(2) to make or give gifts for sale of baby-clothes, handicrafts, jams, cakes, etc.

(3) to distribute posters to libraries, doctors' surgeries, play-groups, schools, nurseries etc.

(4) to do simple administrative work

(5) to help to run local stalls on behalf of Parents Anonymous, who will supply help and guidance

(6) to donate second-hand office equipment – typewriters, filing cabinets, staplers, etc., and, of course, stationery

Parents Anonymous (London), 9 Manor Gardens, Islington, London N7. Tel: 01.263.5672.

PARENTS FOR CHILDREN: Parents for Children are always looking for prospective parents for children with special needs who cannot find homes through conventional adoption agencies. The agency is happy to consider a parent who is disabled, a windowed grandmother, a single man or woman, people with unconventional lifestyles, or would-be parents who are considered by other agencies to be too old to adopt. They are particularly in need of black families for black children. Their slogan is: 'All sorts of children need all sorts of parents.' If you think you could adopt an abused child, a child with physical or mental disabilities or an emotionally troubled child, the address to write to is:

Parents for Children, 222 Camden High Street, London NW1 8QR. Please enclose a s.a.e. Tel: 01.485.7526/7548.

RESPITE CARE: If you can offer a short-break holiday placement (even for a night or two) for a physically or mentally handicapped child, this will provide rest for a family under stress; it may perhaps prevent a breakdown of family relationships. If you can offer RESPITE CARE, contact your local Social Services Department. See your local telephone directory.

SELF-HELP: If you have been abused and feel you could use your experiences constructively to help someone else who has suffered, or may still be suffering, the consequences, enquire from the Citizens' Advice Bureau (see your local telephone directory) if there is a self-help group. If not, you can form one by advertising your intention in your local paper.

STEPNEY CHILDREN'S FUND (Toynbee Hall Children and Families with Special Needs Department) requires volunteers who live in the country and have accommodation to offer a holiday to an underprivileged child in their care. They also require young and energetic volunteers able to make a definite commitment of not less than a month to help with holiday activities such as camps, seaside outings, and to act as escorts etc. They are also urgently in need of girl guide uniforms. Contact:

Director, Bob Le Vaillant, Stepney Children's Fund, 28 Commercial St, London E1 6LS. Tel: 01.247.6943.

* * * * * * * * * *

IF YOUR LIFE IS LIMITED, there are nevertheless many ways you can help to influence changes in the current system of Child Care, or to question that the current care given children is adequate. You can:

1. Write to your local member of Parliament at the House of Commons, Westminster, London S.W.1.

(a) expressing your concern and asking him to use his influence to increase Government funding for all aspects of Child Care; and/or

(b) asking him to support any future Bill relating to improvements to the Children's Act.

2. Write or telephone your local County Councillor asking him when the local Children's Home(s) were last visited by him and if he is personally satisfied with the conditions appertaining. If not, as your representative, what action is he taking to improve matters? Enclose a s.a.e. for his written reply.

3. Write to the Chief Inspector of your local County Constabulory Headquarters (you will find their address in your

238

local telephone directory). Enquire whether your local police force has a representative trained in interviewing abused children. If their reply is in the negative, write to your M.P. expressing your concern.

4. Write to the County Education Officer (see Education Department under your County Council in the telephone directory) and enquire if members of teaching staff in their schools have been alerted to the symptoms of child abuse in their pupils. If the answer is in the negative, request that they should be so alerted and ask for his written confirmation that this will be done.

5. Write to the Director of your local Department of Social Services and enquire how many social workers are fully qualified and how many are partially qualified in the Department, and ask how many cases are currently on their books. If the ratio is greatly in excess of the recommended ratio of thirty cases per social worker, write to your M.P. as per (1) above.

6. Write to the Department of Social Security and ask if all the children 'At Risk' living in your local authority area have been allocated a social worker. If you get no information from them, write to your local Councillor, who is accountable to you, and insist upon a reply. Enclose a s.a.e.

7. Write to any of the Child Care organisations listed above asking for leaflets and posters on child care and abuse, and ask your local doctor's surgery, clinics and other relevant places to display them.

CHILDWATCH will provide an Information Pack called 'The Child Sexual Assault Prevention and Protection Pack' for teachers, child minders or parents. Childwatch, 60 Beck Road, Everthorpe, South Cave, Brough, E. Yorks. Tel: 04302,3824.

8. If you are a good speaker, offer to lecture at your local Women's Institute, British Legion, WRVS etc. Your local library will provide reference books on the subject of child abuse; for titles see the bibliography, page 239. The agencies listed in this appendix will provide leaflets and many will provide speakers, such as Bob Le Vaillant of Stepney Children's Fund (see page 232), who will give talks at Rotary, Round Table, W.I., business lunches and meetings.

9. Invite your local newspaper or radio station to publicise any failure by the authorities you may know about and ask them to air the problem. Media publicity is often the best way to bring about improvements.

*   *   *   *   *   *   *   *   *   *

IF YOU HAVE EVEN THE SLIGHTEST SUSPICION THAT A NEIGHBOUR'S OR FRIEND'S CHILD IS BEING PHYSICALLY OR SEXUALLY ABUSED, NEGLECTED OR EMOTIONALLY DEPRIVED, PLEASE ADVISE SOMEONE WHO CAN INVESTIGATE. The NSPCC guarantee your anonymity and your name will not be revealed. The Social Services Department should also treat your report confidentially, or you may prefer to advise the child's schoolteacher or a Church authority. You could be saving a child unnecessary suffering, or even its life.

Parents, teachers etc. and all those in charge of children can watch specifically for these signs, which indicate a child is possibly being abused: loss of appetite; bedwetting; lack of concentration; sudden behaviour changes; return to babyish ways; lethargy; chronic headaches; stomach troubles; anti-social or overly affectionate behaviour; uncharacteristic flirtatiousness; fear of baby-sitter/friend/relative; pain or discomfort in, or infection of, genital areas. You can ensure that the causes are investigated.

IF YOU HAVE ABUSED A CHILD – OR FEEL YOU MIGHT DO SO – you can obtain help from any of the agencies in Appendix 3.

APPENDIX 3

IF YOU ARE BEING, OR HAVE BEEN, ABUSED AND NEED HELP

The following of names, addresses and telephone numbers are correct at date of publication. HELP, ADVICE, UNDERSTANDING and SUPPORT are available to you from any of these sources:

INCEST CRISIS LINE, P.O. Box 32, Northolt, Middx UB5 4JG. Give a comprehensive 24-hour confidential advice service to all victims of abuse, male or female; and to offenders. Tel: 01.890.4732 or 01.422.5100. Further Crisis Line telephone numbers to ring: London (01) 490.4732; 302.0570; 593.9428. Hull (0482) 445204; Cardiff (0222) 733929; Weymouth (0305) 777385; Slough (0753) 77274; Southend (0702) 584702.
Women with Child Victims: 0965.31432.

RAPE CRISIS CENTRE: P.O. Box 69, London WC1X 9NJ, 24-hour tel: 01.837.1600; 10a.m. – 6p.m., Monday to Friday: 01.278.3956 will provide support and counselling by women for women. They can also provide details of rape crisis centres througout Britain in most major cities.

MOTHERS OF ABUSED CHILDREN, (Incest Crisis Line), 25 Wampool St, Silloth, Cumbria, CA5 4AA. Tel: 0965.31432, will give a counselling service to mothers who know or suspect that their child has been, or is being, sexually abused; or who have themselves been sexually abused in childhood.

THE NATIONAL MARRIAGE GUIDANCE COUNCIL offers regular weekly counselling sessions for couples or individuals whose marriage is in difficulties for any reason, including the long-term consequences of sexual abuse in childhood. There are 160 Marriage Guidance Councils throughout the country. Addresses and telephone numbers can be found in your local telephone directory, or write to: Herbert Gray College, Little Church St., Rugby, Warwickshire, CV21 3AP.

ESTHER RANTZEN'S 'CHILDLINE' offers a counselling service for children who may make a free telephone call by dialling 0800.1111. Adults should write to: Freepost 1111, London EC4B 4BB.

CHILDWATCH works at first hand with the victims of all forms of abuse, referring cases where necessary to the Police, the Social Services and/or the NSPCC.
   Childwatch, 60 Beck Road, Everthorpe, South Cave, Brough, E. Yorks. Tel: 04302.3824.

TABOO, Box No.38, Manchester M60 1HG, offers telephone counselling, advice and information for young women and girls. They will also supply a contact number for a counselling service for men and boys. Sometimes they have places of refuge available for young women between the ages of sixteen and twenty-five. Tel: 061.236.1712. (4 – 8.30 p.m. on Wednesdays) or: Ansaphone manned 24 hours a day: 061.236.1323.

MENTAL HEALTH FOUNDATION are a professionally run body who can put you in touch with an established support group in your area. They have a comprehensive list of 400 such groups covering all areas of the country. Please write to 8 Hallam St, London W1N 6DH, or you can look up your nearest support group in 'The Someone to Talk To Directory', issued by the MHF, which you will find in the reference section in the larger branches of public libraries.

THE NATIONAL CHILDREN'S HOME runs The Family

Network distress phone-in service, with face-to-face group and counselling facilities in 15 centres throughout Great Britain, and a 'touchline' for sexually abused children in Leeds (tel. 457777). For further details write to 85, Highbury Park, London N5 1UD. Tel: 01.226.2033.

THE CHILDREN'S SOCIETY, Church of England Children's Society, Edward Rudolf House, Margery St, London WC1X 0JL; tel: 01.837.4299, have a network of family and neighbourhood centres throughout England and Wales. For details check in your local telephone directory. The Society also has a safe house for young runaways called the Central London Teenage Project: many of the young people have experienced sexual or physical abuse. Tel: 01.639.1466.

NSPCC: The National Society for the Prevention of Cruelty to Children aims to protect children from abuse, and prevent child abuse in all its forms. The Society provides a 24-hour service to children and families in England, Wales and Northern Ireland. If you need help or know of a child who needs help you will find the address and telephone number of your nearest NSPCC office in your local telephone directory.

RSSPCC: The Royal Scottish Society for the Protection of Cruelty to Children offer the same support as the NSPCC. They provide counselling for adult and child victims of sexual abuse and for parents of children who have been abused. Telephone counselling is available on Mondays and Wednesdays until 9 p.m. Tel: 041.556.1156. For further informations write to 15, Annfield Place, Glasgow, G31 2XE, or look up your nearest branch in the local telephone directory.

FAMILY PLANNING CLININCS. Your local CLINIC offers free, special counselling for people with sexual problems stemming from childhood abuse. See under FAMILY PLAN-NING in your local directory for telephone number and address.

BRITISH ASSOCIATION FOR COUNSELLING are a

professionally run body who provide an Information Service on counselling agencies and counsellors covering Great Britain. 371, Sheep St, Rugby, Warwickshire, CV21 3BX. Tel: 0788.78328/9.

SAMARITANS: You will find their telephone number and address listed in your local telephone directory under 'SAMARITANS The'. Their telephone is manned 24 hours a day.

Your DOCTOR will obtain appropraite help for you.

Your CITIZENS' ADVICE BUREAU or the LIBRARY will supply you with alist of Self-Help Groups in your locality, where you can meet with others with similar experiences to your own.

READING LISTS on sexual abuse of children are available from the NSPCC, 67 Saffron Hill, London EC1N 8RS.

Bibliography

H. Argent, *Find Me a Family, The Story of Parents for Children*, Souvenir Press, 1984.

E. Bass & L. Thornton (eds.), *I Never Told Anyone, Writings by Women Survivors of Child Sexual Abuse*, Harper & Row, 1983

P. Beezley Mrazek, *Sexually Abused Children and Their Families*, Pergamon Press, 1981

A. Bignell, *Hopping Down in Kent*, Hale, 1977

V. Carver, *Child Abuse: A Study Text*, Open University Press, 1978

B. Copper, *Werewolf, in Legend, Fact & Art*, St Martin's Press, New York, 1977

M. Elliott, *Preventing Child Sexual Assault, A Practical Guide to Talking with Children*, Bedford Square Press, 1985

S. Forward & C. Buck, *Betrayal of Innocence, Incest & Its Devastation*, Penguin, revised edition, 1981

N. Frude, *Psychological Approaches to Child Abuse*, Batsford Academic, 1980

R. Inglis, *Sins of the Fathers, A Study of the Physical & Emotional Abuse of Children*, Peter Owen 1978

R. S. & C. H. Kempe, *Child Abuse, The Developing Child*, Open Books, 1978

C. M. Lee, *Child Abuse: A Reader and Source Book*, The Open University Press, 1978

S. Nelson, *Incest, Fact & Myth*, Stramullion, 1982

L. Pincus & C. Dare, *Secrets in the Family*, Faber & Faber, 1978

R. Porter (ed.), *Child Sexual Abuse Within the Family*, The CIBA Foundation, Tavistock Publications, 1984

P. E. Quinn, *Cry Out*, Abingdon Press, Nashville, 1984

J. Renvoize, *Children in Danger*, Routledge & Kegan Paul, 1974

J. Renvoize, *Incest, A Family Pattern*, Routledge & Kegan Paul, 1982

J. Renvoize, *Web of Violence: A Study of Family Violence*, Routledge & Kegan Paul, 1978

H. Tunnicliffe, *Custodianship*, Pepar Publications, 1986

H. Tunnicliffe, *The Law Says...*, Pepar Publications, 1985

Acknowledgements

I would like to thank the following people for their assistance in providing research material for this book and for giving me an insight into their personal and working relationships with Jeanette: Joyce Nash, Pat Verity, Carol Sinker, Bob Le Vaillant, Margaret Kaye, Nigel Evans, Peter Stickings, Ken Start, Pam Walker, Trevor Hart, Rosemary Wolfson and Dr Stephen Wolfkind. I would also like to thank the Director of the Mental Health Foundation, the staff of the N.S.P.C.C., Tower Hamlets Social Services Department and Dr Barnardo's for the further information so willingly provided.

I am as always indebted to East Grinstead and Edenbridge Public Libraries for their help in selecting relevant background reading.

I would like to thank William Heinemann Ltd for giving permission to quote from 'The Prophet' by Kahlil Gibran; all the publishers who have allowed me to quote from their books relevant extracts for my chapter headings; and the London Evening Standard, Raissa Page and H Tempest Ltd for permission to reproduce photographs.

Most of all, I am deeply indebted to Jeanette and the children for allowing me to tell their story.

Photographic Acknowledgements

The author and publishers wish to thank Raissa Page of Format Photographers Ltd. for permission to reproduce photographs.